CLIVE BARKE
He is the author o
The Damnation Ga … *ut, The Great*
and Secret Show, The … *ound Heart, Imajica* and
The Thief of Always. In addition to his work as a novelist and short story writer, he also illustrates, writes, directs and produces for the stage and screen. His spectacular films the*Hellraiser* trilogy, *Nightbreed* and *Candyman* bring his unique and indelible vision of modern horror to celluloid and video life. Barker uses all aspects of popular culture to substantiate his extraordinary insight into the menacing present. Millions of readers and filmgoers have been captivated by Barker's prodigious talents; now graphic novel adaptations of his stories add a further dimension to his hold on the popular imagination. Clive Barker lives in Los Angeles, where he continues his love affair with the bizarre, the perverse and the terrifying.

INTERNATIONAL ACCLAIM FOR
CLIVE BARKER:

'Barker is so good I am almost tongue-tied. What Barker does makes the rest of us look like we've been asleep for the last ten years.'

STEPHEN KING

'A powerful and fascinating writer with a brilliant imagination.'

J.G.BALLARD

'Clive Barker has been an amazing writer from his first appearance, with great gifts of invention and commitment to his own vision stamped on every page.'

PETER STRAUB

BOOKS BY CLIVE BARKER

The Books of Blood (*six volumes*)
The Damnation Game
Weaveworld
Cabal
The Great and Secret Show
The Hellbound Heart
Clive Barker Illustrator
Imajica
The Thief of Always

GRAPHIC STORIES BY CLIVE BARKER

The Yattering and Jack
Tapping the Vein (*four volumes*)
Son of Celluloid

THE ARTISTS

Lionel Talaro

was born June 2 1960, in San Diego, California, where he still resides. He attended San Diego City College and Southern California Art Institute in Calabassas, where he developed his technique, a combination of gouache and pencil on gessoed board. Since 1986, he has created illustrations for advertising and a wide variety of publications. *Revelations* marks his comics debut. He is illustrating the upcoming Clive Barker graphic novel *Sex, Death and Starshine.*

Hector Gomez

was born in Argentina and now lives in Brazil. He has illustrated the Clive Barker stories *How Spoilers Bleed* and *New Murders in the Rue Morgue*, and has had two graphic novels published in Brazil, *Samsara* and *Amazing Muchachas.* He works as an illustrator for mainstream magazines and exhibits canvases at exhibitions. His covers for Malibu Comics include *Dollman, Rocket Ranger, Jungle Love* and *Paranoia.*

CLIVE BARKER

REVELATIONS

Illustrated by Lionel Talaro
Adapted by Steve Niles

AND

BABEL'S CHILDREN

Illustrated by Hector Gomez
Adapted by Fred Burke

EclipseGraphicNovels
An Imprint of HarperCollins*Publishers*

Eclipse Graphic Novels
An Imprint of HarperCollins*Publishers*,
77–85 Fulham Palace Road,
Hammersmith, London W6 8JB

Published by Eclipse Graphic Novels 1993

9 8 7 6 5 4 3 2 1

ISBN 0 586 21756 8

Printed and bound in Hong Kong

THERE HAD BEEN TALK OF TORNADOES IN AMARILLO, OF CATTLE, CARS, AND SOMETIMES ENTIRE HOUSES LIFTED UP AND DASHED TO THE EARTH AGAIN, OF WHOLE COMMUNITIES LAID WASTE IN A FEW DEVASTATING MOMENTS.
PERHAPS THAT WAS WHAT MADE VIRGINIA SO UNEASY TONIGHT.

EITHER THAT OR THE ACCUMULATED FATIGUE OF TRAVELING SO MANY EMPTY HIGHWAYS WITH JUST THE DEADPAN SKIES OF TEXAS FOR SCENERY...
...AND NOTHING TO LOOK FORWARD TO AT THE END OF THE NEXT LEG OF THE JOURNEY BUT ANOTHER ROUND OF HYMNS AND HELLFIRE.

HER SPINE ACHING, SHE TRIED HER BEST TO GET SOME SLEEP.
BUT THE HOT, STILL AIR CLUNG AROUND HER NECK AND GAVE HER DREAMS OF SUFFOCATION.

SHE GAVE UP HER ATTEMPT TO REST AND CONTENTED HERSELF WITH WATCHING THE FIELDS PASS AND COUNTING THE GRAIN ELEVATORS BRIGHT AGAINST THE GATHERING THUNDERHEADS.

IN THE FRONT, EARL SANG TO HIMSELF AS HE DROVE. BESIDE HER, JOHN--NO MORE THAN TWO FEET AWAY BUT TO ALL INTENTS AND PURPOSES A MILLION MILES AWAY--STUDIED THE EPISTLES OF ST. PAUL.

THE STORM CAME SUDDENLY AS EVENING FELL, LENDING DARKNESS TO DARKNESS, INSTANTLY PLUNGING THE AMARILLO-PAMPA HIGHWAY INTO WATERY NIGHT.
THE RAIN, THOUGH REFRESHING, HAD SOAKED THE ONLY DRESS JOHN APPROVED OF HER WEARING AT MEETINGS. UNEASE GREW IN HER WITH EVERY MILE THEY COVERED TO PAMPA, LISTENING TO THE VEHEMENCE OF THE DOWNPOUR ON THE ROOF...
...AND TO HER HUSBAND, JOHN, SPEAKING IN WHISPERS AT HER SIDE.
WHEREFORE HE SAITH. AWAKE THOU THAT SLEEPEST...
...AND RISE FROM THE DEAD, AND CHRIST SHALL GIVE THEE LIGHT.
SEE THEN THAT YE WALK CIRCUMSPECTLY, NOT AS FOOLS, BUT AS WISE...

REDEEMING THE TIME, BECAUSE THE DAYS ARE EVIL.
HE SURELY KNEW THE PASSAGES HE WAS READING BY HEART. HE QUOTED THEM OFTEN ENOUGH, AND WITH SUCH A MIXTURE OF FAMILIARITY AND FRESHNESS THAT THE WORDS MIGHT HAVE BEEN HIS, NOT PAUL'S.

THAT PASSION AND VIGOR WOULD MAKE JOHN GYER AMERICA'S GREATEST EVANGELIST, VIRGINIA HAD NO DOUBT OF THAT.
DURING THE GRUELING, HECTIC WEEKS OF THE TRI-STATE TOUR, HER HUSBAND HAD DISPLAYED UNPRECEDENTED CONFIDENCE AND MATURITY.
HIS MESSAGE HAD LOST NONE OF ITS VEHEMENCE WITH THIS NEWFOUND PROFESSIONALISM--IT WAS STILL THAT OLD FASHIONED MIXTURE OF DAMNATION AND REDEMPTION THAT HE ALWAYS PROPOUNDED--BUT NOW HE HAD COMPLETE CONTROL OF THE GIFT.

IN TOWN AFTER TOWN--IN OKLAHOMA AND NEW MEXICO AND NOW IN TEXAS--THE FAITHFUL HAD GATHERED IN THE HUNDREDS AND THOUSANDS TO LISTEN, EAGER TO COME AGAIN INTO GOD'S KINGDOM.
IN PAMPA, THIRTY FIVE MILES FROM HERE, THEY WOULD ALREADY BE ASSEMBLING, DESPITE THE RAIN, DETERMINED TO HAVE A GRANDSTAND VIEW WHEN THE CRUSADER ARRIVED.
THEY WOULD HAVE BROUGHT THEIR CHILDREN, THEIR SAVINGS, AND MOST OF ALL, THEIR HUNGER FOR FORGIVENESS.
BUT FORGIVENESS WAS FOR TOMORROW. FIRST THEY HAD TO GET TO PAMPA, AND THE RAIN WAS WORSENING. EARL WAS FORCED TO CONCENTRATE ALL HIS ATTENTION ON THE ROAD AHEAD.
VIRGINIA TRIED NOT TO CONCERN HERSELF WITH THE WAY HE WAS DRIVING, BUT AS THE TORRENT BECAME A DELUGE, HER ANXIETY GOT THE BETTER OF HER.
THE LORD IS WITH US.
IT'S A BAD NIGHT, JOHN. MAYBE WE SHOULDN'T TRY TO GO ALL THE WAY TO PAMPA. EARL MUST BE TIRED.
I'M FINE. IT'S NOT THAT FAR.

YOU'RE TIRED. WE ALL ARE.
WE'LL FIND A MOTEL. EARL CAN CALL AHEAD TO PAMPA AND TELL THEM THAT WE'LL BE WITH THEM IN THE MORNING. HOW'S THAT?

WHATEVER YOU SAY, BOSS. I THINK WHITE DEER'S NEXT OFF THE HIGHWAY. MAYBE THEY'LL HAVE A MOTEL.

IN FACT, THE COTTONWOOD MOTEL LAY A HALF MILE WEST OF WHITE DEER, IN AN AREA OF WASTEGROUND SOUTH OF U.S. 60.
COTTONWOOD MOTEL
Office
I HOPE THERE'S SPACE FOR US.
GYER DIDN'T REPLY.

TALK TO ME, JOHN.
WHAT FOR?
NEVER MIND. I JUST HATE THE RAIN.

IT WON'T LAST ALL NIGHT.
RUNNING HIS HAND THROUGH HIS HAIR WAS A GESTURE HE USED ON THE PLATFORM AS PUNCTUATION, A PAUSE BETWEEN ONE MOMENTOUS STATEMENT AND THE NEXT.

SHE KNEW HIS RHETORIC, BOTH PHYSICAL AND VERBAL, SO WELL.
SOMETIMES SHE THOUGHT SHE KNEW EVERY-THING ABOUT HIM THERE WAS TO KNOW; THAT HE HAD NOTHING LEFT TO TELL HER THAT SHE TRULY WANTED TO HEAR.

BUT THEN THE SENTIMENT WAS PROBABLY MUTUAL. THEY HAD LONG AGO CEASED TO HAVE A MARRIAGE RECOGNIZABLE AS SUCH.

TONIGHT THEY WOULD LIE IN SEPARATE BEDS, AND HE WOULD SLEEP THAT DEEP, EASY SLEEP THAT CAME READILY TO HIM, WHILE SHE SURREPTITIOUSLY SWALLOWED A PILL OR TWO TO BRING SOME WELCOME SERENITY.

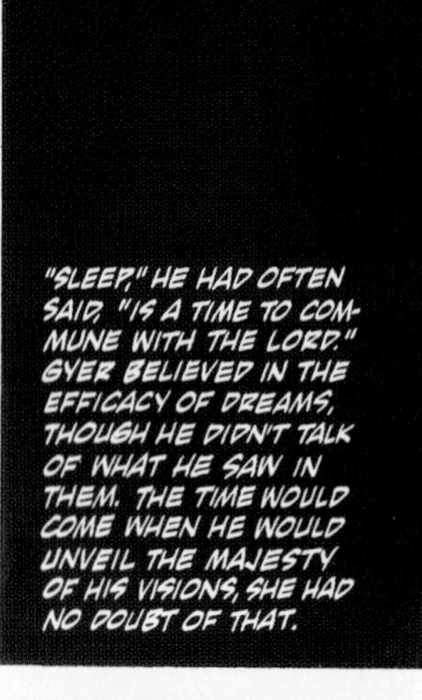
"SLEEP," HE HAD OFTEN SAID, "IS A TIME TO COMMUNE WITH THE LORD." GYER BELIEVED IN THE EFFICACY OF DREAMS, THOUGH HE DIDN'T TALK OF WHAT HE SAW IN THEM. THE TIME WOULD COME WHEN HE WOULD UNVEIL THE MAJESTY OF HIS VISIONS, SHE HAD NO DOUBT OF THAT.

ROOMS SEVEN AND EIGHT. I GOT THE KEY TO THE INTERCONNECTING DOOR, TOO.
GOOD.

LAST TWO IN THE PLACE. I'LL DRIVE THE CAR AROUND. THE ROOMS ARE AT THE FAR END.

THE INTERIOR OF THE TWO ROOMS WAS A HYMN TO BANALITY.
THEY'D STAYED IN WHAT SEEMED LIKE A THOUSAND CELLS LIKE THESE.
DAMN.
JOHN WAS INSENSITIVE TO HIS SURROUNDINGS, BUT TO VIRGINIA'S EYES THESE ROOMS WERE AN APT MODEL FOR PURGATORY. SOULLESS LIMBOS IN WHICH NOTHING HAD HAPPENED, NOR EVER WOULD.

THERE WAS NOTHING TO MARK THESE ROOMS OUT AS DIFFERENT FROM ALL THE OTHERS.

BUT THERE WAS SOMETHING DIFFERENT IN **HER** TONIGHT.

IT WASN'T TALK OF TORNADOES THAT HAD BROUGHT THIS STRANGENESS ON. SHE FELT ODDLY REMOVED FROM HERSELF, AS THOUGH SHE WERE WATCHING EVENTS THROUGH A VEIL DENSER THAN THE WARM RAIN FALLING OUTSIDE THE DOOR.

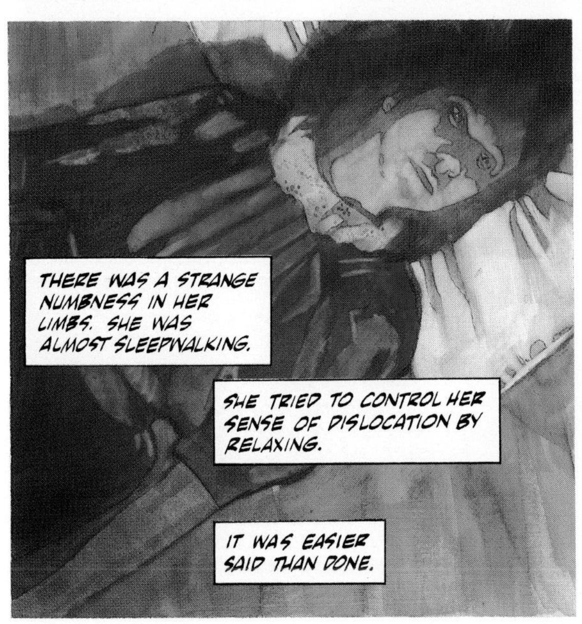
THERE WAS A STRANGE NUMBNESS IN HER LIMBS. SHE WAS ALMOST SLEEPWALKING.
SHE TRIED TO CONTROL HER SENSE OF DISLOCATION BY RELAXING.
IT WAS EASIER SAID THAN DONE.

SOMEBODY HAD A TELEVISION ON IN A NEARBY ROOM, AND THE LATE-NIGHT MOVIE WAS WORD-FOR-WORD CLEAR THROUGH THE PAPER THIN WALLS.
ARE YOU ALL RIGHT?

EARL, EVER SOLICITOUS.
YES, I'M FINE, THANK YOU. A LITTLE THIRSTY.

I'LL SEE IF I CAN GET SOMETHING FOR YOU TO DRINK. THEY PROBABLY HAVE A COKE MACHINE.

SHE NODDED, MEETING HIS EYES. THERE WAS A SUBTEXT TO THIS EXCHANGE WHICH GYER COULD NOT KNOW. ON AND OFF THROUGHOUT THE TOUR EARL HAD SUPPLIED VIRGINIA WITH PILLS.
NOTHING EXOTIC, JUST TRANQUILIZERS TO SOOTH HER INCREASINGLY JANGLED NERVES. BUT THEY--LIKE STIMULANTS, MAKEUP, AND JEWELRY--WERE NOT LOOKED KINDLY UPON BY A MAN OF GYER'S PRINCIPLES.
WHEN, BY CHANCE, HER HUSBAND HAD DISCOVERED THE DRUGS, THERE HAD BEEN AN UGLY SCENE. EARL HAD TAKEN THE BRUNT OF HIS EMPLOYER'S IRE, FOR WHICH VIRGINIA WAS DEEPLY GRATEFUL.
THOUGH EARL WAS UNDER STRICT INSTRUCTIONS NEVER TO REPEAT THE CRIME, HE WAS SOON SUPPLYING HER AGAIN. THEIR GUILT WAS AN ALMOST PLEASURABLE SECRET BETWEEN THEM. SHE READ COMPLICITY IN HIS EYES, AS HE DID IN HERS.

"NO COCA-COLA FOR HER, EARL."
WELL, I JUST THOUGHT WE COULD MAKE AN EXCEPTION...
EXCEPTION?
THE LORD DOESN'T GIVE US LAWS TO LIVE BY SO THAT WE CAN MAKE EXCEPTIONS, EARL. YOU KNOW BETTER THAN THAT.
RHETORIC WAS IN THE AIR, AND EARL CURSED HIS IDIOT TONGUE.

AT THAT MOMENT EARL DIDN'T MUCH CARE WHAT THE LORD DID OR SAID. HIS CONCERN WAS FOR VIRGINIA.

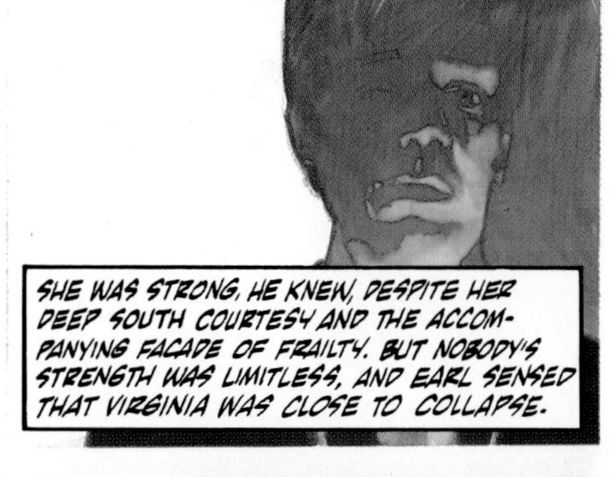
SHE WAS STRONG, HE KNEW, DESPITE HER DEEP SOUTH COURTESY AND THE ACCOMPANYING FACADE OF FRAILTY. BUT NOBODY'S STRENGTH WAS LIMITLESS, AND EARL SENSED THAT VIRGINIA WAS CLOSE TO COLLAPSE.

"MAYBE YOU COULD GET ME SOME ICE WATER?"
ICE WATER, COMING RIGHT UP.
SHE GAVE SO MUCH TO HER HUSBAND. MORE THAN ONCE IN THE PAST WEEKS OF THE TOUR EARL HAD THOUGHT THAT PERHAPS SHE DESERVED BETTER.
7

WHY DON'T YOU CALL THE OFFICE AND HAVE SOMEONE BRING IT OVER? I WANT TO GO THROUGH NEXT WEEK'S ITINERARY WITH YOU.
"IT'S NO PROBLEM..."
...REALLY. BESIDES, I SHOULD CALL PAMPA, AND TELL THEM WE'RE DELAYED.

HE NEEDED AN EXCUSE TO HAVE SOME TIME TO HIMSELF. THE ATMOSPHERE BETWEEN VIRGINIA AND GYER WAS DETERIORATING BY THE DAY.
THE COTTONWOOD TREE IN THE MIDDLE OF THE LOT HUNG ITS BALDING HEAD IN THE FURY OF THE DELUGE. HE KNEW EXACTLY HOW IT FELT.

EARL STOOD ON THE WALKWAY WONDERING HOW HE WOULD BE ABLE TO KEEP HIS SANITY IN THE LAST EIGHT WEEKS OF THE TOUR.
HE DIDN'T SEE THE TWO FIGURES, THOUGH THE PATH THEY TOOK TO ROOM SEVEN LED THEM DIRECTLY ACROSS HIS LINE OF VISION.

THEY WALKED THROUGH THE DRENCHING RAIN FROM THE WASTEGROUND BEHIND THE MANAGER'S OFFICE--WHERE, BACK IN 1955, THEY HAD PARKED THEIR RED BUICK.
THOUGH THE RAIN FELL IN A STEADY TORRENT, IT LEFT THEM BOTH UNTOUCHED.

THE WOMAN SLOWED FOR A MOMENT TO STARE AT THE MAN WHO WAS WATCHING THE COTTONWOOD TREE WITH SUCH RAPT ATTENTION. HE HAD KIND EYES, DESPITE THE FROWN.
IN HER TIME SHE MIGHT HAVE LOVED SUCH A MAN, BUT THEN HER TIME HAD LONG GONE, HADN'T IT?

SADIE DURNING LOOKED AT HER HUSBAND. THE YEARS HAD NOT TEMPERED THE RESENTMENT SHE FELT TOWARD HIM, ANY MORE THAN THEY'D IMPROVED HIS SHIFTY FEATURES OR HIS TOO-EASY LAUGH.

SHE HAD NOT MUCH LIKED HIM ON JUNE 2, 1955, AND SHE DIDN'T MUCH LIKE HIM NOW, PRECISELY THIRTY YEARS ON.

BUCK DURNING HAD THE SOUL OF A PHILANDERER, AS HER FATHER HAD ALWAYS WARNED HER. THAT IN ITSELF WAS NOT SO TERRIBLE; IT WAS PERHAPS THE MASCULINE CONDITION.

BUT IT HAD LED TO SUCH GRUBBY BEHAVIOR THAT EVENTUALLY SHE HAD TIRED OF HIS ENDLESS DECEPTIONS.

I'LL JUST WASH OFF MY EQUIPMENT, AND BE RIGHT WITH YA.
UH-HUH.

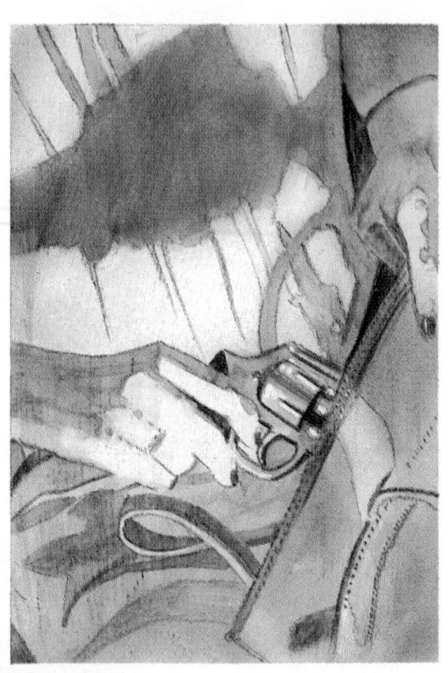

KLIK

BLAM

SHE HAD RUN, THROWING THE GUN AWAY AS SHE WENT, KNOWING THE POLICE WERE BOUND TO CATCH HER, AND WHEN THEY DID... SHE DIDN'T CARE.

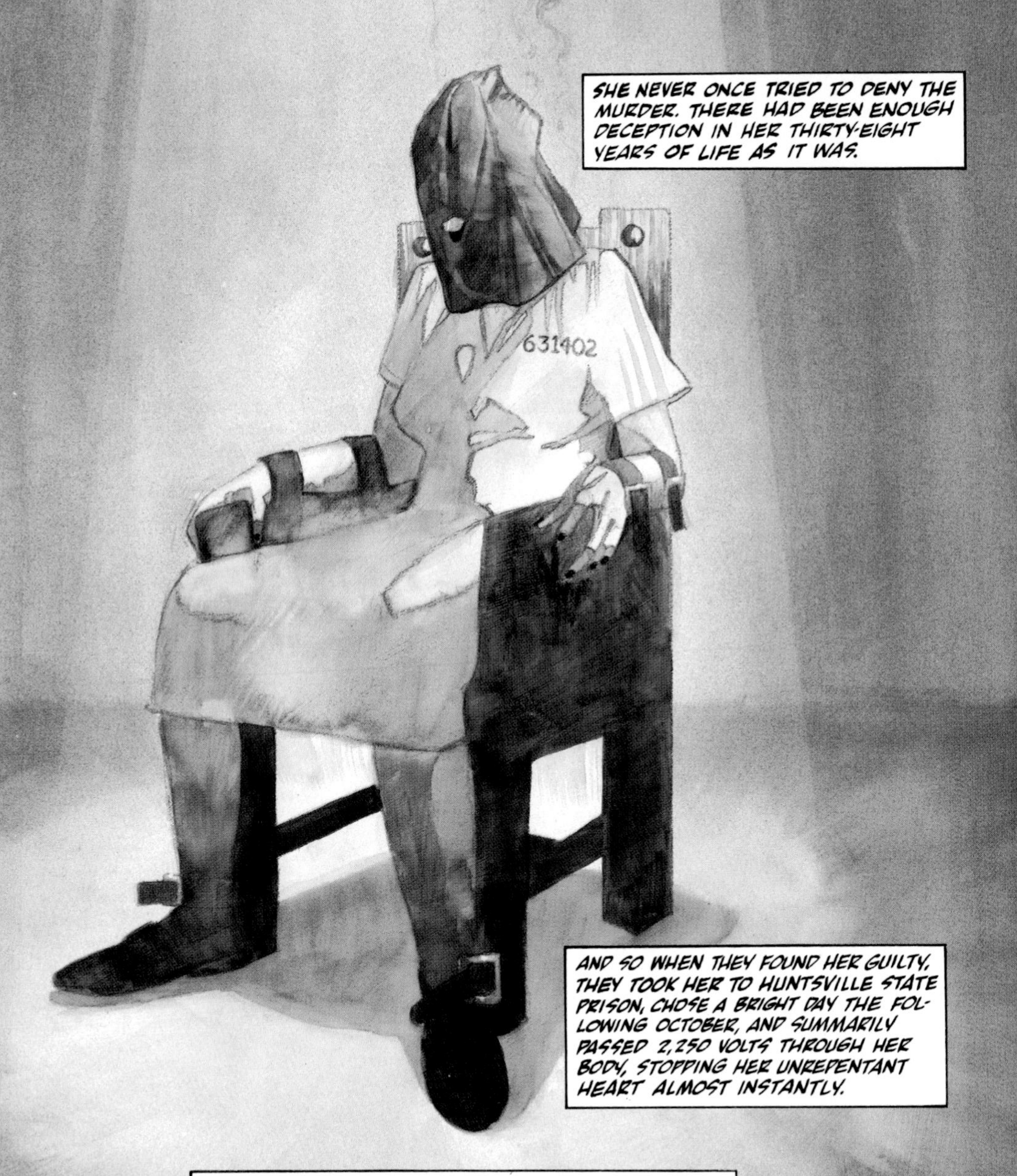
THEY HAD TAKEN HER TO THE CARSON COUNTY JAIL, AND, AFTER A FEW WEEKS, TO TRIAL.
SHE NEVER ONCE TRIED TO DENY THE MURDER. THERE HAD BEEN ENOUGH DECEPTION IN HER THIRTY-EIGHT YEARS OF LIFE AS IT WAS.
631402
AND SO WHEN THEY FOUND HER GUILTY, THEY TOOK HER TO HUNTSVILLE STATE PRISON, CHOSE A BRIGHT DAY THE FOLLOWING OCTOBER, AND SUMMARILY PASSED 2,250 VOLTS THROUGH HER BODY, STOPPING HER UNREPENTANT HEART ALMOST INSTANTLY.
AN EYE FOR AN EYE; A TOOTH FOR A TOOTH. SHE HAD BEEN BROUGHT UP WITH SUCH SIMPLE EQUATIONS. SHE'D NOT BEEN UNHAPPY TO DIE BY THE SAME MATHEMATICS.

THE OCCUPANCY WAS NOT A PROBLEM. SADIE HAD LONG BECOME USED TO THE ETHEREAL STATE, TO WANDERING UNSEEN AMONG THE LIVING. IN SUCH A CONDITION SHE HAD ATTENDED HER NIECE'S WEDDING, AND LATER ON HER FATHER'S FUNERAL, STANDING BESIDE THE GRAVE WITH THE DEAD OLD MAN AND GOSSIPING ABOUT THE MOURNERS.

AS SADIE MOVED THROUGH THE WALL AND INTO THE ROOM IN WHICH THEIR FATAL FARCE HAD BEEN PLAYED OUT, SHE WONDERED IF THE SHOT HAD HURT HIM VERY MUCH.

SHE MUST ASK HIM TONIGHT, SHE THOUGHT, SHOULD THE OPPORTUNITY ARISE.

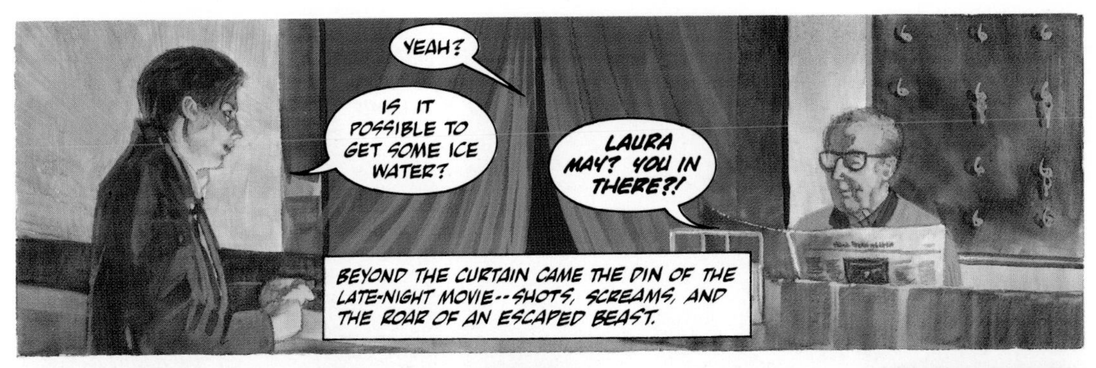
YEAH?
IS IT POSSIBLE TO GET SOME ICE WATER?
LAURA MAY? YOU IN THERE?!
BEYOND THE CURTAIN CAME THE DIN OF THE LATE-NIGHT MOVIE-- SHOTS, SCREAMS, AND THE ROAR OF AN ESCAPED BEAST.

WHAT DO YOU WANT, PA?
THERE'S A MAN WANT'S ROOM SERVICE. WILL YOU GET OUT HERE AND SERVE HIM?
NO REPLY CAME; JUST MORE SCREAMS.
free take one
SO, YOU WITH THE EVANGELIST?

YES...HOW DID YOU KNOW IT WAS...?
LAURA MAY RECOGNIZED HIM. SEEN HIM IN THE PAPER.
THAT SO?
free take one
DON'T MISS A TRICK, MY BABY.

AS IF ON CUE, LAURA MAY EMERGED.
HUH...

AND WHEN HER EYES FELL ON EARL SHE VISIBLY BRIGHTENED.
...OH. WHAT CAN I DO FOR YOU, MISTER?
THE LINE, COUPLED WITH HER SMILE, SEEMED TO SIGNAL MORE THAN JUST POLITE INTEREST.
OR WAS THAT JUST WISHFUL THINKING?
TAKING A CHANCE, HE RETURNED THE SMILE.

ICE WATER. I WAS WONDERING IF YOU HAD ANY? MRS. GYER ISN'T FEELING SO WELL.
YES...

I'LL GET SOME.
THE DIN OF THE MOVIE ABATED--A SCENE OF CALM, PERHAPS, BEFORE THE BEAST EMERGED AGAIN--AND IN THE HUSH EARL COULD HEAR THE RAIN BEATING DOWN OUTSIDE, TURNING THE EARTH TO MUD.
QUITE A GULLY WASHER TONIGHT, EH? THIS KEEPS UP, YOU BE RAINED OUT TOMORROW.

PEOPLE COME OUT IN ALL KINDS OF WEATHER. JOHN GYER'S A BIG DRAW.
WOULDN'T RULE OUT A TORNADO. YEAR BEFORE LAST, WIND TOOK THE ROOF RIGHT OFF THE SCHOOL.

HERE WE ARE, I'LL TAKE IT MYSELF. YOU LEAD ON.
UH.
HE DIDN'T OBJECT. IT WOULD GIVE THEM A LITTLE WHILE TO EXCHANGE PLEASANTRIES AS THEY WALKED TO THE GYERS' ROOM. PERHAPS THE SAME THOUGHT WAS IN HER MIND.

EITHER THAT, OR SHE WANTED A CLOSER VIEW OF THE EVANGELIST.
SHALL I CARRY THE JUG? YOU BRING THE GLASSES AND TRAY.
SURE... WHAT'S YOUR NAME?
EARL. EARL RAYBURN.

I'M LAURA MAY CADE.
PLEASED TO MEET YOU, LAURA MAY CADE.

YOU KNOW ABOUT THIS PLACE, DO YOU? PAPA TOLD YOU, I SUPPOSE.
YOU MEAN THE TORNADOES?
NO. I MEAN MURDER.

WHAT'S THE PROBLEM?
NO PROBLEM.
I DON'T WANT TO SHARE A ROOM WITH THESE TWO.
WELL, THIS IS THE ROOM WHERE...WHERE WE STAYED.

LET'S GO BACK IN THE OTHER ROOM. WE'LL HAVE MORE PRIVACY.
THEY CAN'T SEE US.
BUT I CAN SEE THEM, AND IT GIVES ME THE CREEPS. IT'S NOT GOING TO MATTER IF WE'RE IN A DIFFERENT ROOM, FOR CHRIST'S SAKE.

ARE YOU COMING OR NOT?
IT WAS BETTER TO GIVE WAY TO HIM. IF SHE STARTED TO ARGUE NOW THEY'D NEVER GET PAST THE FIRST HURDLE.

CONCILIATION WAS THE KEYNOTE OF THIS REUNION, SADIE REMINDED HERSELF, FOLLOWING BUCK INTO ROOM EIGHT.
VIRGINIA THOUGHT ABOUT GETTING UP AND GOING INTO THE BATHROOM WHERE SHE COULD TAKE ONE OR TWO TRANQUILIZERS, BUT JOHN'S PRESENCE FRIGHTENED HER.

SOMETIMES SHE FELT HE COULD SEE RIGHT INTO HER, THAT ALL HER PRIVATE GUILT WAS AN OPEN BOOK TO HIM. SHE WAS CERTAIN THAT IF SHE GOT UP NOW, AND ROOTED THROUGH HER BAG FOR MEDICATION, HE WOULD ASK HER WHAT SHE WAS DOING.
SHE'D BLURT THE TRUTH OUT FOR SURE. SHE DIDN'T HAVE THE STRENGTH TO RESIST THE HEAT OF THOSE ACCUSING EYES.

THERE WAS AN EVASIVE QUALITY TO THE LIGHT IN THE ROOM. IT DISTRESSED HER, AND SHE WANTED TO CLOSE HER LIDS AGAINST ITS TRICKS.
ONLY MOMENTS BEFORE, THE LIGHT HAD CONJURED A MIRAGE AT THE END OFF THE BED; A MOUTH-WING FLICKER OF SUBSTANCE THAT HAD ALMOST CONGEALED IN THE AIR BEFORE FLITTING AWAY.

...AND THERE CAME OUT OF THE SMOKE LOCUSTS UPON THE EARTH...
SHE INSTANTLY RECOGNIZED THE PASSAGE; ITS IMAGERY WAS UNMISTAKABLE.
...AND UNTO THEM WAS GIVEN POWER, AS THE SCORPIONS OF THE EARTH HAVE POWER.
THE VERSE WAS FROM THE REVELATIONS OF ST. JOHN THE DIVINE. HE HAD DECLAIMED THEM TIME AFTER TIME AT MEETINGS.

AND IT WAS COMMANDED THEM...
GYER LOVED REVELATIONS. ITS POETRY, INSTEAD OF COMING OUT OF HIM, CAME **THROUGH** HIM. HELPLESS IN ITS GRIP, HE ROSE ON A SPIRAL OF EVER MORE AWESOME METAPHOR.

USUALLY, TO HEAR HER HUSBAND SPEAK THE POEMS OF REVELATIONS WAS A JOY TO VIRGINIA, BUT NOT TONIGHT.

TONIGHT THE WORDS SEEMED RIPE TO THE POINT OF CORRUPTION.
UH...
WHAT IS IT?
DOES MY READING DISTURB YOU?
NOTHING.
THE INQUIRY WAS A CHALLENGE.
SHE SENSED, PERHAPS FOR THE FIRST TIME, THAT HE DIDN'T REALLY UNDERSTAND WHAT HE WAS SAYING, THAT THE SPIRIT OF THE WORDS PASSED HIM BY WHILE HE RECITED THEM.
NO, NO OF COURSE NOT.

THE WOMAN WAS LYING, OF COURSE; THE WORDS DID DISTURB HER. THEY DISTURBED SADIE, TOO. BUT ONLY BECAUSE THEY SEEMED SO PITIFULLY MELODRAMATIC, A DRUG-DREAM OF ARMAGEDDON, MORE COMICAL THAN INTIMIDATING.
TELL HIM. GO ON. TELL HIM YOU DON'T LIKE IT.
AND THE SHAPES OF THE LOCUSTS WERE UNTO HORSES PREPARED UNTO BATTLE AND...

...ON THEIR HEADS WERE CROWNS LIKE GOLD, AND THEIR FACES WERE...
WHO ARE YOU TALKING TO? THEY CAN'T HEAR YOU.
GO ON. TELL THE BASTARD HOW RIDICULOUS HE SOUNDS.
COMIC BOOK TERRORS, FIT TO SCARE CHILDREN WITH. WHY DID PEOPLE HAVE TO DIE TO GROW OUT OF THAT KIND OF NONSENSE?

SAY IT. SAY IT.
JOHN?
DO YOU HAVE TO TALK ABOUT DEATH ALL THE TIME? IT'S VERY DEPRESSING.
WHAT DID YOU SAY?

THOSE PASSAGES YOU READ. I HATE THEM. THEY'RE SO...
STUPID.
...UNPLEASANT.
SADIE, ARE YOU COMING TO BED OR NOT?

IN A MOMENT. I JUST WANT TO SEE WHAT HAPPENS IN HERE.
THIS IS THE INSPIRED WORD OF THE LORD, VIRGINIA.
I KNOW, JOHN, BUT THERE **ARE** OTHER PASSAGES.

I THOUGHT YOU **LIKED** THE APOCALYPSE.
NO, IT DISTRESSES ME.
YOU'RE TIRED.
OH, YES, THAT'S WHAT THEY ALWAYS TELL YOU WHEN YOU GET TOO CLOSE TO THE TRUTH. NEXT HE'LL TELL HER TO TAKE A NAP.
WHY DON'T YOU SLEEP FOR A WHILE? I'LL GO NEXT DOOR AND WORK.

YES, I **AM** TIRED.
FOOLISH WOMAN. FIGHT BACK, OR HE'LL DO THE SAME AGAIN.

WE'RE HERE TO MAKE FRIENDS, SO LET'S **GET** TO IT.
THERE'S NO NEED FOR VIOLENCE, BUCK.
HA! THAT'S RICH, COMING FROM YOU.

YOU WANT TO SEE VIOLENCE?

THIS IS VIOLENCE!

IT CERTAINLY WAS A PERMANENT MARK. ABOUT THE ONLY ONE SHE'D EVER MADE ON THE MAN, SHE SUSPECTED.
YOU SEE THAT, SWEETHEART? YOU MADE THAT.
YOU CHEATED FROM THE BEGINNING, DIDN'T YOU?
WE'RE NOT TALKING ABOUT CHEATING HERE--WE'RE TALKING ABOUT SHOOTING.
SEEMS TO ME ONE SUBJECT LEADS TO THE OTHER. AND BACK AGAIN.

ALL RIGHT. I HAD WOMEN. SO WHAT?
SO I SHOT YOU FOR IT.
THAT WAS ABOUT ALL SHE HAD TO SAY ON THE SUBJECT. IT HAD MADE FOR A SHORT TRIAL.
WELL, AT LEAST YOU COULD TELL ME YOU'RE SORRY.

BUT I'M NOT!
THIS WHOLE THING IS USELESS. YOU PRIED INTO MY BUSINESS, YOU SNOOPED AROUND BEHIND MY BACK--
I DID NOT SNOOP. YOUR DIRT CAME AND FOUND ME.
DIRT?!

OH YES, DIRT. IT ALWAYS WAS WITH YOU. FURTIVE AND SWEATY.
TAKE THAT BACK!
YOU USED TO FRIGHTEN ME ONCE, BUT THEN I BOUGHT A GUN.

ALL RIGHT, DON'T SAY I DIDN'T TRY. I WANTED TO SEE IF WE COULD FORGIVE AND FORGET, I REALLY DID. BUT YOU'RE NOT WILLING TO GIVE AN INCH, ARE YOU?
WE COULD HAVE HAD A GOOD TIME HERE TONIGHT, BABE. JUST YOU AND ME.

I COULD HAVE GIVEN YOU A BIT OF THE OLD JAZZ, YOU KNOW WHAT I MEAN? TIME WAS, YOU WOULDN'T HAVE SAID NO.
.....
WHAT HE SAID WAS TRUE. TIME WAS SHE WOULD HAVE TAKEN WHAT LITTLE HE GAVE HER AND COUNTED HERSELF A BLESSED WOMAN. BUT TIMES HAD CHANGED.
COME ON, BABE. LOOSEN UP.

SHE WAS ABOUT TO REPLY TO HIS SUGGESTION WHEN IN CAME THE MAN WITH SOULFUL EYES ACCOMPANIED BY A WOMAN WHOSE FACE RANG A BELL IN SADIE'S MEMORY.
WHAT SAY WE FORGET WHAT YOU SAID AND LIE DOWN AND TALK?
ICE WATER.
GOING TO GET UNDRESSED?
IN A MINUTE, BUCK. WE'VE GOT ALL NIGHT, FOR CHRIST'S SAKE.
I'M LAURA MAY CADE.
OF COURSE. YOU'RE LITTLE LAURA MAY.
THE GIRL HAD BEEN FIVE OR SIX WHEN SADIE WAS LAST HERE; AN ODD, SECRETIVE CHILD, FULL OF SLY LOOKS.
IT'S REAL NICE HAVING YOU FOLKS HERE. WE DON'T GET MUCH HAPPENING HERE. JUST THE OCCASIONAL TORNADO...
GYER NODDED TO EARL, WHO PRODUCED A FIVE DOLLAR BILL AND GAVE IT TO LAURA MAY. SHE THANKED HIM, SAYING IT WASN'T NECESSARY, THEN TOOK THE BILL.
SHE WASN'T TO BE BRIBED INTO LEAVING, HOWEVER.
THIS KIND OF WEATHER MAKES PEOPLE FEEL REAL PECULIAR...
EARL COULD PREDICT WHAT SUBJECT WAS HOVERING BEHIND HER LIPS. HE'D ALREADY HEARD THE BONES OF THE STORY ON THE WAY TO THE ROOM, AND KNEW VIRGINIA WAS IN NO MOOD TO HEAR SUCH A TALE.
THANK YOU FOR THE WATER--
MY WIFE'S BEEN SUFFERING FROM HEAT EXHAUSTION.
YOU SHOULD BE CAREFUL, MA'AM. PEOPLE DO SOME MIGHTY WEIRD THINGS--
LIKE WHAT?
OH, MURDER MOSTLY.

MURDER?
HEAR THAT? SHE REMEMBERS.
IN THIS VERY ROOM.

WAIT, EARL! I WANT TO HEAR WHAT HAPPENED.
NO, YOU DON'T.
OH YES, SHE DOES. YOU'D REALLY LIKE TO KNOW, WOULDN'T YOU GINNY?

FOR A MOMENT PREGNANT WITH POSSIBILITIES, VIRGINIA TURNED AND LOOKED STRAIGHT THROUGH THE INTERCONNECTING DOOR. THE LOOK WAS SO DIRECT IT COULD ALMOST HAVE BEEN ONE OF RECOGNITION.
WHAT'S WRONG?
THERE'S SOMEBODY HERE, JOHN. THERE'S SOMEBODY IN THE ROOM WITH US. I HEARD VOICES BEFORE. RAISED VOICES.

NEXT DOOR.
NO, FROM EARL'S ROOM. AND I SAW SOMETHING AT THE END OF THE BED... SOMETHING IN THE AIR.
OH, JESUS, THE GODDAMN WOMAN'S PSYCHIC.
WOW, REALLY?
HUSH. SHE SAID SHE COULD SEE US.
YOU'RE NOT WELL, VIRGINIA. IT'S THOSE PILLS HE FED YOU...
NO. WHEN WILL YOU STOP TALKING ABOUT THE PILLS? THEY WERE JUST TO CALM ME DOWN, HELP ME SLEEP.
SHE CERTAINLY ISN'T CALM NOW. SHE COULD USE SOME OF THE OLD JAZZ--NOW, THAT WOULD HELP HER SLEEP.

I TELL YOU I CAN SEE THINGS.
THAT I CAN'T? IS THAT WHAT YOU'RE SAYING? THAT YOU CAN SEE VISIONS THE REST OF US ARE BLIND TO?
I'M NOT PROUD OF IT, DAMN YOU.

COME AWAY, BUCK. WE'RE UPSETTING HER. SHE KNOWS WE'RE HERE.
SO WHAT? HER PRICK HUSBAND DOESN'T BELIEVE HER. HE THINKS SHE'S CRAZY.
WELL, WE'LL MAKE HER CRAZY IF WE PARADE AROUND. LET'S AT LEAST KEEP OUR VOICES DOWN, HUH?

WANT TO MAKE IT WORTH MY WHILE? I'LL KEEP OUT OF THE WAY IF YOU AND ME CAN HAVE SOME FUN.
ALL RIGHT, BUCK. JUST LET ME FRESHEN UP AND FIX MY HAIR.
IT WAS PERVERSE TO REJECT BUCK'S ADVANCES. THE MAN WAS AN EMOTIONAL INFANT AND ALWAYS HAD BEEN. SEX WAS ONE OF THE FEW WAYS HE COULD EXPRESS HIMSELF.

I'M GOING TO TAKE A SHOWER, VIRGINIA. I SUGGEST YOU LIE DOWN AND STOP MAKING A FOOL OF YOURSELF. YOU GO TALKING LIKE THAT IN FRONT OF PEOPLE AND YOU'LL JEOPARDIZE THE CRUSADE.
YOU HEAR ME?
OH, YES...

SLAM!
...I HEAR YOU.
THERE WASN'T A TRACE OF FEELING TO BE FOUND IN HER VOICE.

THE ICE IN THE JUG HAD LONG SINCE MELTED. THE WATER SHE DRANK WAS TEPID, LIKE THE RAIN THAT FELL RELENTLESSLY OUTSIDE. BY MORNING, PERHAPS THE WHOLE WORLD WOULD HAVE BEEN WASHED AWAY.
IF IT HAD, SHE MUSED, SHE WOULDN'T GRIEVE.

I ASKED YOU NOT TO MENTION THE KILLING. MRS. GYER CAN'T TAKE THAT KIND OF TALK.
PEOPLE ARE GETTING KILLED ALL THE TIME. CAN'T GO AROUND WITH HER HEAD IN A BUCKET.

I'M SORRY. I DIDN'T MEAN TO GET YOU INTO TROUBLE.
SURE, I KNOW. I'M JUST EDGY.
IT'S THE HEAT. PUTS THOUGHTS INTO PEOPLE'S HEADS. YOU KNOW.
EARL COULD FEEL THE BACK OF HIS NECK TINGLE. THIS WAS HIS CUE, WASN'T IT?

DO YOU HAVE TO GO BACK THERE RIGHT NOW?
NO, I'M BEST LEAVING THEM TO SORT IT OUT IN PEACE. THEY DON'T WANT ME.
WELL, I DO.

WHY DON'T WE GO TO MY ROOM? I DON'T LIKE IT OUT HERE.
WHAT ABOUT YOUR PAPA?

HE'LL BE DEAD DRUNK BY NOW. JUST TAKE IT QUIETLY. HE'LL NEVER KNOW.
EARL WASN'T VERY HAPPY WITH THIS GAME PLAN. IT WAS MORE THAN HIS JOB WAS WORTH TO BE FOUND IN BED WITH LAURA MAY. HE WAS A MARRIED MAN, EVEN IF HE HADN'T SEEN BARBARA IN THREE MONTHS.

DON'T COME IF YOU DON'T WANT TO.
IT'S NOT THAT.

IN A SENSE, THOUGH EARL COULDN'T KNOW IT AT THE TIME, ALL THAT LAY AHEAD--THE FARCE, THE BLOODLETTING, THE INEVITABLE TRAGEDY-- PIVOTED ON LAURA MAY UNCONSCIOUSLY WETTING HER LOWER LIP.
AH, **SHIT.** YOU'RE TOO MUCH, LAURA MAY, YOU KNOW THAT?

SOMEWHERE OVER TOWARD SKELLYTOWN THE CLOUDS GAVE OUT A LOUD ROLL OF THUNDER, LIKE A CIRCUS DRUMMER BEFORE SOME PARTICULARLY ELABORATE ACROBATICS.

WHAT IS THAT WOMAN DREAMING ABOUT?
WHO ARE YOU?
SADIE FOUGHT THE TEMPTATION TO GO NEXT DOOR AND WHISPER IN THE DREAMER'S EAR.

MURDER!
FOR GOD'S SAKE, SOMEBODY STOP THEM!
MURDER!

HER HEAD FELT SO LIGHT IT MIGHT FLOAT OFF LIKE A BALLOON. SELDOM IN HER LIFE HAD SHE FELT SO STRANGE.

IT WAS AS THOUGH SHE WAS LOSING HER SLENDER GRIP ON WHAT WAS REAL, AS THOUGH THE SOLID WORLD WERE SLIPPING THROUGH HER FINGERS.
IN THE BATHROOM SHE COULD HEAR JOHN SPEAKING ALOUD--ADDRESSING THE MIRROR, NO DOUBT, TO REFINE EVERY DETAIL OF HIS DELIVERY.
SHE NEEDED SOME AIR.

THERE WAS SOME REFRESHMENT TO BE HAD OUTSIDE, BUT PRECIOUS LITTLE.
BUT I DON'T WAAAAANT TO GO TO BED!! PLEEEEE--
YOU HEARD WHAT I SAID!

FOR MAYBE TEN SECONDS THE VOICE WAS HUSHED. THEN IT BEGAN AGAIN, IN A HIGHER KEY.
MOMEEEEEEE!
GO ON, YOU CRY. THERE'S PLENTY OF REASON.

SHE TRUSTED UNHAPPINESS IN PEOPLE. MORE AND MORE IT WAS ALL SHE TRUSTED. SADNESS WAS SO MUCH MORE HONEST THAN THE ARTIFICIAL BONHOMIE THAT WAS ALL THE STYLE THESE DAYS, THAT FACADE OF EMPTY-HEADED OPTIMISM THAT WAS PLASTERED OVER THE DESPAIR THAT EVERYONE FELT IN THEIR HEART OF HEARTS.
THE CHILD WAS EXPRESSING THAT WISE PANIC NOW, AS IT CRIED IN THE NIGHT. SHE SILENTLY APPLAUDED ITS HONESTY.

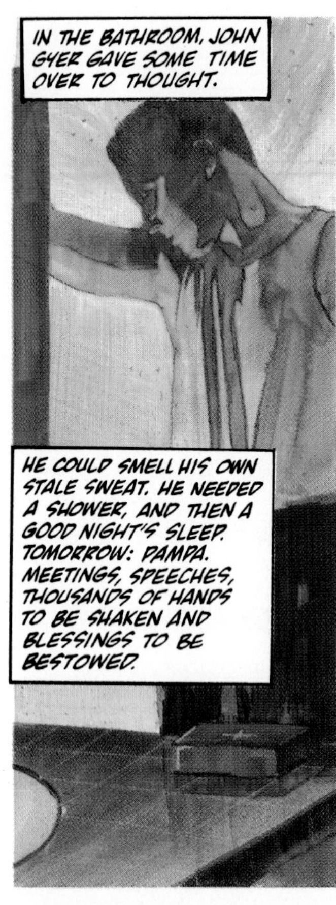
IN THE BATHROOM, JOHN GYER GAVE SOME TIME OVER TO THOUGHT.
HE COULD SMELL HIS OWN STALE SWEAT. HE NEEDED A SHOWER, AND THEN A GOOD NIGHT'S SLEEP. TOMORROW: PAMPA. MEETINGS, SPEECHES, THOUSANDS OF HANDS TO BE SHAKEN AND BLESSINGS TO BE BESTOWED.

SOMETIMES HE FELT SO TIRED, AND THEN HE'D GET TO WONDERING IF THE LORD COULDN'T LIGHTEN HIS BURDEN A LITTLE. BUT THAT WAS THE DEVIL TALKING IN HIS EAR, WASN'T IT?
HE KNEW BETTER THAN TO PAY THAT SCURRILOUS VOICE MUCH ATTENTION. IF YOU LISTENED ONCE, THE DOUBTS WOULD GET HOLD...THE WAY THEY HAD OF VIRGINIA.

HE WOULD HAVE TO BRING HER BACK TO THE PATH OF THE RIGHTEOUS, MAKE HER SEE THE DANGER HER SOUL WAS IN. THERE WOULD BE TEARS AND COMPLAINTS; MAYBE SHE WOULD BE BRUISED A LITTLE.
BUT BRUISES HEAL.

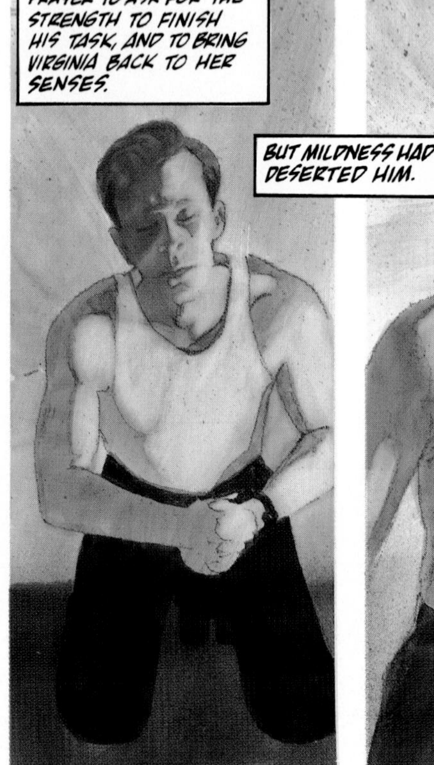
HE TRIED TO FIND SOME BENIGN WORDS, A GENTLE PRAYER TO ASK FOR THE STRENGTH TO FINISH HIS TASK, AND TO BRING VIRGINIA BACK TO HER SENSES.
BUT MILDNESS HAD DESERTED HIM.

IT WAS THE VOCABULARY OF REVELATIONS THAT CAME BACK TO HIS LIPS, UNBIDDEN. HE LET THE WORDS SPILL OUT, EVEN THOUGH THE FEVER IN HIM BURNED BRIGHTER WITH EVERY SYLLABLE HE SPOKE.

WHAT DO YOU THINK?
THE BEDROOM, IT SEEMED, WAS A MAUSOLEUM FOUNDED IN THE NAME OF TRIVIA.
THIS IS MY COLLECTION.
THE THOUGHT THAT THIS WAS ALL LAURA MAY'S DOING SHRANK EARL'S STOMACH. THE WOMAN WAS CLEARLY VERGING ON LUNACY.
SO I SEE.
I'VE BEEN COLLECTING SINCE I WAS SIX. EVERYBODY LEAVES SOMETHING BEHIND. EVEN IF IT'S ONLY A DEAD MATCH OR A TISSUE WITH LIPSTICK ON IT. WE USED TO HAVE A MEXICAN GIRL, OPHELIA, WHO CLEANED ROOMS WHEN I WAS A CHILD.
IT STARTED AS A GAME, REALLY. SHE'D ALWAYS BRING ME SOMETHING FROM THE GUESTS WHO'D LEFT. WHEN SHE DIED, I TOOK OVER COLLECTING.

EARL BEGAN TO GRASP THE ABSURD POETRY OF THE MUSEUM. IN LAURA MAY'S NEAT BODY WAS ALL THE AMBITION OF A GREAT CURATOR.
NOT FOR HER MERE ART. SHE WAS COLLECTING KEEPSAKES OF A MORE INTIMATE NATURE,

YOU'VE GOT IT ALL MARKED.
OH, YES. IT WOULDN'T BE MUCH USE IF I DIDN'T KNOW WHO IT ALL BELONGED TO, NOW WOULD IT?
INCREDIBLE.
HE SUSPECTED SHE DIDN'T SHOW HER COLLECTION TO MANY PEOPLE. HE FELT ODDLY HONORED TO BE VIEWING IT.

I'VE GOT SOME REALLY PRIZE THINGS, STUFF I DON'T PUT ON DISPLAY.
OH?

THE TISSUE PAPER THAT LINED THE DRAWER RUSTLED AS SHE SHOWED HIM HER SELECTION OF SPECIAL ACQUISITIONS...
...AN EMPTY BOOK OF MATCHES, WHICH SHE HAD TRACED TO A HOMOSEXUAL BAR IN AMARILLO, DISCARDED BY Y...
...A HEROIN NEEDLE CARELESSLY LEFT BY X...
...A SOILED TISSUE FOUND BENEATH THE BED OF A HOLLYWOOD STAR WHO HAD TRAGICALLY DIED SIX WEEKS AFTER STAYING AT THE MOTEL...

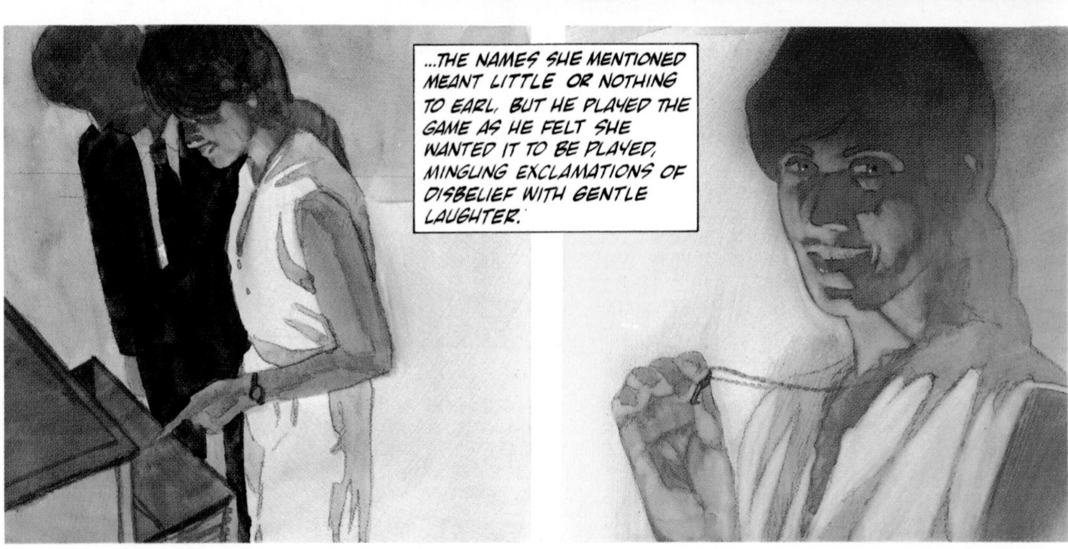
...THE NAMES SHE MENTIONED MEANT LITTLE OR NOTHING TO EARL, BUT HE PLAYED THE GAME AS HE FELT SHE WANTED IT TO BE PLAYED, MINGLING EXCLAMATIONS OF DISBELIEF WITH GENTLE LAUGHTER.

I WASN'T QUITE TELLING YOU THE TRUTH BEFORE, WHEN I SAID IT BEGAN AS A GAME WITH OPHELIA. THAT REALLY CAME LATER.
SO WHAT STARTED YOU OFF?

A SMITH AND WESSON .38, IN PRISTINE CONDITION. IT TOOK EARL ONLY A MOMENT TO REALIZE WHICH MOTEL GUEST THIS PIECE OF HISTORY HAD BELONGED TO.
THE GUN THAT SADIE DURNING USED...
I FOUND IT IN THE SCRUB BEHIND THE MOTEL, BEFORE THE POLICE GOT TO SEARCHING FOR IT. THERE WAS SUCH A COMMOTION THAT NIGHT THAT NOBODY LOOKED TWICE AT ME. AND OF COURSE THEY DIDN'T TRY TO LOOK FOR IT IN THE LIGHT.

WHY WAS THAT?
THE '55 TORNADO HIT, JUST THE DAY AFTER. WE HAD FUNERALS FOR WEEKS.
BUT YOU SHOULD'VE TURNED IT IN! IT'S EVIDENCE.
SADIE ADMITTED IT ALL, RIGHT FROM THE BEGINNING. IT WOULDN'T HAVE MADE ANY DIFFERENCE.

THAT'S BLOOD ON IT THERE. IT WAS STILL WET WHEN I FOUND IT. SHE MUST HAVE TOUCHED BUCK'S BODY TO MAKE SURE HE WAS DEAD. ONLY USED TWO BULLETS. THE REST ARE STILL IN THERE.
I'VE NEVER SEEN ANYTHING LIKE THIS PLACE.

YOU'RE QUITE A WOMAN. YOU KNOW THAT?

I'M GLAD YOU LIKE WHAT YOU SEE.

SADIE...? ARE YOU COMING TO BED OR NOT?
I JUST WANT TO FINISH FIXING MY HAIR.
YOU'RE NOT PLAYING FAIR. FORGET YOUR HAIR AND COME OVER HERE.
YOU'RE IN NO HURRY, ARE YOU, BUCK? I MEAN, YOU'RE NOT GOING ANYWHERE?

YOU THINK IT'S FUNNY, DON'T YOU? ME GETTING SHOT. YOU GETTING THE CHAIR. IT GIVES YOU SOME KIND OF PERVERSE SATISFACTION.
SHE THOUGHT ABOUT THIS FOR A FEW MOMENTS. IT WAS THE FIRST TIME BUCK HAD SHOWN ANY REAL DESIRE TO TALK SERIOUSLY. SHE WANTED TO ANSWER WITH THE TRUTH.
YES. YES, I SUPPOSE IT DID PLEASE ME, IN AN ODD SORT OF WAY.
I *KNEW* IT!

DID IT HURT MUCH?
ARE YOU KIDDING? WHAT DOES IT FUCKING LOOK LIKE?
I THOUGHT IT WOULD BE QUICK. I NEVER WANTED YOU TO SUFFER.
IS THAT RIGHT?
OF COURSE. I LOVED YOU ONCE, BUCK. I REALLY DID. YOU KNOW WHAT THE HEADLINE WAS THE DAY AFTER?
NO, I WAS OTHERWISE ENGAGED, REMEMBER?
"MOTEL BECOMES SLAUGHTERHOUSE OF LOVE," IT SAID. I THOUGHT IT WAS KIND OF ROMANTIC. THERE WERE PICTURES OF THE ROOM, THE BLOOD ON THE FLOOR, AND OF YOU BEING CARRIED OUT UNDER A SHEET.
MY FINEST HOUR, AND I DON'T EVEN GET MY FACE IN THE PRESS.

OH, YEAH? DID THEY COME AND VISIT YOU? GIVE YOU A BIT OF THE OLD JAZZ TO KEEP YOUR MIND OFF THE BIG DAY?
NO.
JUST THINKING ABOUT IT'S GETTING ME COOKING, SADIE. WHY DON'T YOU COME AND GET IT WHILE IT'S HOT?
I GOT THREE HUNDRED PROPOSALS OF MARRIAGE WHILE I WAS WAITING FOR THE CHAIR-- DID I EVER TELL YOU THAT?
WE CAME HERE TO TALK, BUCK.
WE TALKED, FOR CHRIST'S SAKE. I DON'T WANT TO TALK NO MORE. NOW COME HERE. YOU PROMISED.

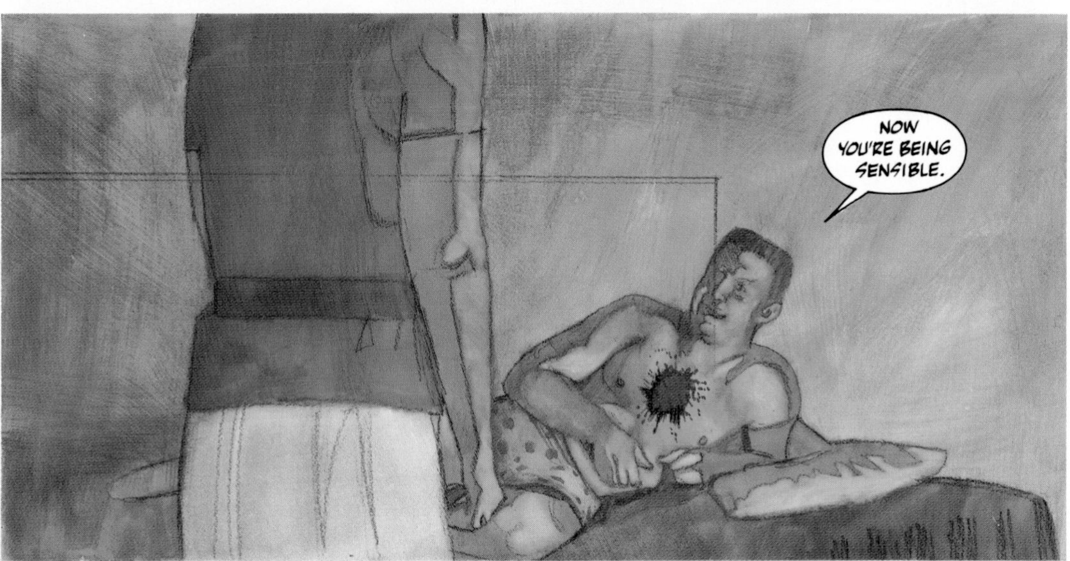
NOW YOU'RE BEING SENSIBLE.

THE RAIN HAD COOLED VIRGINIA'S FACE SOMEWHAT, AND THE TRANQUILIZERS SHE'D TAKEN WERE FINALLY BEGINNING TO SOOTHE HER SYSTEM. IN THE BATHROOM, JOHN WAS STILL PRAYING, HIS VOICE RISING AND FALLING.
AS SHE WATCHED THE RAIN, VIRGINIA THOUGHT SHE HEARD A GROAN FROM THE NEXT ROOM.

SHE FROZE. THE GROAN CAME AGAIN, LOUDER. SHE FELT HERSELF BEGIN TO TREMBLE.

GIVE A LITTLE, DAMN YOU...
THE WORDS, THOUGH BLURRED, WERE UNMISTAKABLE.
PLAY THE GAME, WILL YOU?
THERE WAS ANGER IN THOSE WORDS.

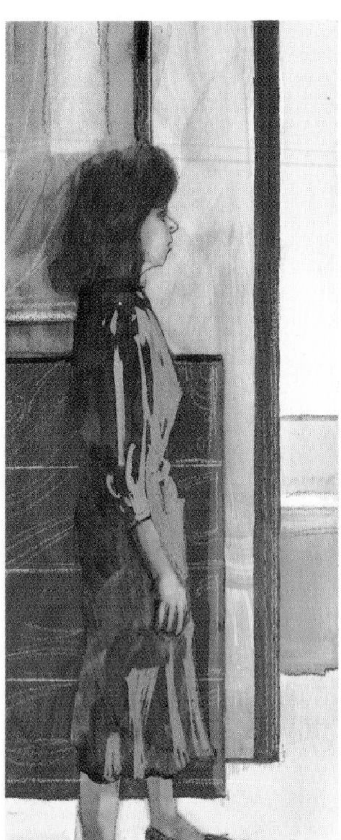

VIRGINIA LOOKED THROUGH INTO ROOM EIGHT. THERE WAS A SHADOW ON THE BED. IT WRITHED DIS-TRESSINGLY, AS IF ATTEMPTING TO DEVOUR ITSELF.
MORE VOICES ROSE FROM THE SHADOW. NOT ONE VOICE THIS TIME, BUT TWO.

THE WORDS WERE JUMBLED. IN HER GROWING PANIC SHE COULD MAKE LITTLE SENSE OF THEM. SHE COULDN'T TURN HER BACK ON THE SCENE, HOWEVER. SHE STARED, TRYING TO MAKE SENSE OF THE SHIFTING CONFIGURATION.
A SMATTERING OF WORDS CAME CLEAR, AND WITH THEM, A RECOGNITION.

SHE HEARD A WOMAN'S VOICE PROTESTING. SHE EVEN BEGAN TO SEE THE SPEAKER, STRUGGLING BENEATH A PARTNER.
HER FIRST INSTINCT HAD BEEN CORRECT. IT WAS A DEVOURING, OF A KIND.

THAT BASTARD GRIN OF HIS MADE SADIE'S TRIGGER FINGER ITCH.
THIS IS WHAT HE'D COME FOR TONIGHT. NOT FOR CONVERSATION ABOUT FAILED DREAMS, BUT TO HUMILIATE HER THE WAY HE HAD SO OFTEN IN THE PAST, WHISPERING OBSCENITIES INTO HER NECK WHILE HE PINNED HER TO THE SHEETS.

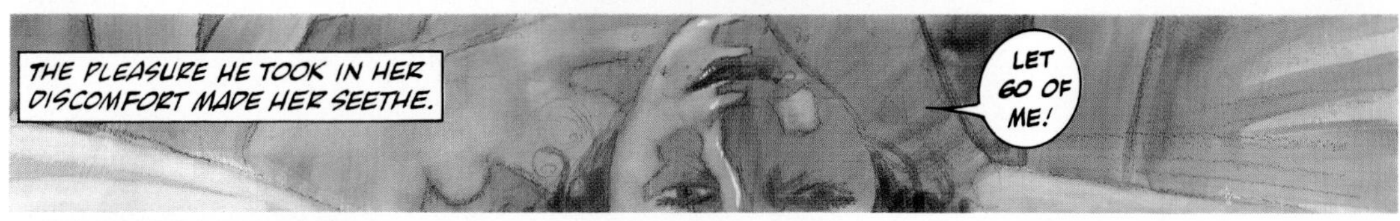
THE PLEASURE HE TOOK IN HER DISCOMFORT MADE HER SEETHE.
LET GO OF ME!

LET HER ALONE.
WELL, WE'VE GOT AN AUDIENCE.

HOW MUCH CAN SHE SEE OR HEAR? ENOUGH TO KNOW WHO WE ARE?
COME ON. IT'S ONLY THE CRAZY LADY.
KEEP AWAY FROM ME.
YOU CAN'T HARM ME NOW, WOMAN. I'M ALREADY DEAD, REMEMBER?
WHAT LITTLE CHANCE OF RECONCILIATION THERE HAD BEEN HAD DEGENERATED INTO A BLOODY FARCE. THE ONLY SOLUTION FOR SADIE WAS TO GET OUT, LEAVING POOR VIRGINIA TO MAKE WHAT SENSE OF IT SHE COULD.

THE LONGER SHE STAYED TO FIGHT WITH BUCK, THE WORSE THE SITUATION WOULD BECOME FOR ALL THREE OF THEM.
WHERE ARE YOU GOING?
OUT.

I SAID
I LOVED YOU,
BUCK, DIDN'T I?
WELL, MAYBE
I DID.
BUT
I'M CURED
NOW.
GOODBYE,
BUCK. HAVE A NICE
ETERNITY.
BITCH!
WORTHLESS
BITCH!
VIRGINIA WATCHED THE SHADOW PASS THROUGH THE CLOSED DOOR AND HELD ONTO THE TATTERED REMAINS OF HER SANITY WITH WHITE-KNUCKLED FISTS.

SHE HAD TO PUT THESE APPARITIONS OUT OF HER HEAD AS QUICKLY AS POSSIBLE OR SHE KNEW SHE'D GO CRAZY.
WHAT SHE NEEDED NOW WAS PILLS.

THE TATTOO OF THE RAIN ON THE ROOF SOUNDED LOUDER AND LOUDER IN HER HEAD.

A ROLL OF THUNDER GAVE WEIGHT TO THE PERCUSSION.
KRACK
AND THEN, JOHN'S VOICE.

WHAT ARE YOU DOING, VIRGINIA?
I... I... HEARD THE VOICES AGAIN.

WOMAN, HAVEN'T YOU LEARNED YOUR LESSON? WHERE DID YOU GET THE PILLS, VIRGINIA?
EARL AGAIN, I SUPPOSE. WHO ELSE?

NO.
DON'T LIE TO ME, VIRGINIA! YOU KNOW THE LORD HEARS YOUR LIES, AS I HEAR THEM. AND YOU ARE JUDGED, VIRGINIA! JUDGED!
PLEASE LEAVE ME BE.
YOU'RE POISONING YOURSELF.

I NEED THEM, JOHN. I REALLY DO.
SHE HAD NO ENERGY TO HOLD HIS BULLYING AT BAY, NOR DID SHE WANT HER PILLS TAKEN FROM HER. BUT HE WOULD HAVE HIS WAY, AS ALWAYS.
LOOK AT YOURSELF, GROVELING ON THE FLOOR.
DON'T START ON ME, JOHN. YOU WIN. TAKE THE PILLS. GO ON! TAKE THEM!

IS THIS ALL?
YES.
HE WAS CLEARLY DISAPPOINTED BY HER RAPID CAPITULATION,

EARL WILL BE SORRY. I PROMISE YOU THAT. HE'S EXPLOITED YOUR WEAKNESS--
...NO!
--YOUR WEAKNESS AND YOUR FEAR. THE MAN IS IN SATAN'S EMPLOY, THAT MUCH IS APPARENT.

DON'T TALK NONSENSE! I ASKED HIM TO SUPPLY THEM. HE DIDN'T WANT TO DEFY YOU, JOHN. IT WAS ME ALL ALONG.
NO. YOU WON'T SAVE HIM. NOT THIS TIME. HE'S WORKED TO SUBVERT ME ALL ALONG. I SEE THAT NOW. WORKED TO HARM MY CRUSADE THROUGH YOU. WELL I'M WISE TO HIM NOW. OH YES. OH YES!

WHERE IS HE?! GONE FOR MORE OF THE SAME FILTH?
NO! I DON'T KNOW WHERE HE'S GONE.
YOU PRAY, WOMAN. YOU GET DOWN ON YOUR KNEES AND THANK THE LORD I'M HERE TO SAVE YOU FROM SATAN.

HER BLEARY EYES CAME TO REST ON A FEW TABLETS STILL ON THE FLOOR. ALL WAS NOT QUITE LOST.
BUT, SOMEONE HAD THEIR EYES ON HER.

HER HEART SEEMED TO LOSE ITS RHYTHM AS SHE REMEMBERED THE SHADOWS IN THE ROOM NEXT DOOR. THERE HAD BEEN TWO. ONE HAD DEPARTED, BUT THE OTHER...?

IT WAS STARING AT HER. SHE COULD SEE ITS EYES. HER TENU-OUS GRASP OF ITS EXISTENCE WAS IMPROVING.

AND THEN, AS HER OUTSTRETCHED HAND BRUSHED AGAINST ITS SMOKE FORM, AN ENTIRE PORTRAIT OF HER ACCOSTER SPRANG INTO VIEW IN FRONT OF HER.
WAS THIS MORE OF HER DREAM, SPILLING INTO THE LIVING WORLD?

PERHAPS JOHN HAD BEEN CORRECT ALL ALONG.
PERHAPS SHE **HAD** INVITED THIS LUNACY TO HERSELF WITH THE VERY TABLETS SHE WAS EVEN NOW TREADING TO POWDER UNDERFOOT.
WAS IT HER IMAGINATION, OR HAD IT OPENED ITS ARMS, AS IF TO EMBRACE HER?

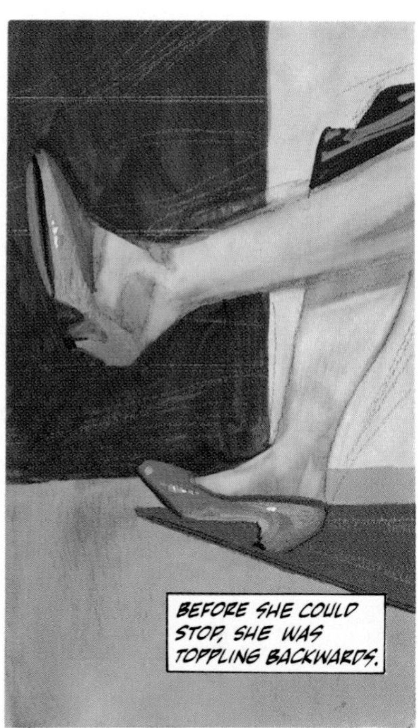
BEFORE SHE COULD STOP, SHE WAS TOPPLING BACKWARDS.

AGAIN SHE MADE CONTACT WITH THE DREAM-THING; AGAIN THE WHOLE HORRID PICTURE APPEARED IN FRONT OF HER. BUT THIS TIME IT DIDN'T DISAPPEAR, BECAUSE THE APPARITION HAD SNATCHED AT HER HAND AND WAS GRASPING IT TIGHT.
UNABLE TO RESIST, SHE MET ITS GAZE. THEY WERE NOT THE DEVIL'S EYES. THEY WERE STUPID, EVEN COMICAL.
SUDDENLY SHE WAS NOT AFRAID. THIS WAS NO DEMON. IT WAS A DELUSION, BROUGHT ON BY EXHAUSTION AND PILLS. IT COULD DO HER NO HARM.
THAT'S BETTER. YOU JUST WANT A BIT OF THE OLD JAZZ, DON'T YOU, GINNIE?
HE WASN'T CERTAIN IF SHE HEARD HIM, BUT NO MATTER. HE COULD READILY MAKE HIS INTENTIONS APPARENT.
YOU DON'T EXIST. YOU'RE ONLY IN MY MIND, LIKE JOHN SAID. THE PILLS MADE YOU. THE PILLS DID IT ALL.
YOU'RE NOT REAL, ARE YOU? I'M RIGHT, AREN'T I?
CERTAINLY. I'M JUST A DREAM, THAT'S ALL.
NO NEED TO FIGHT ME, IS THERE? I'LL HAVE COME AND GONE BEFORE YOU KNOW IT.

EARL!
OFFICE
HE HAD LEFT THEIR ROOM WITH THE GIRL WHO'D BROUGHT THE ICE WATER, AND THEY CERTAINLY WOULDN'T BE TAKING A WALK TOGETHER IN WEATHER LIKE THIS.
THE THUNDER HAD MOVED IN CLOSER IN THE LAST FEW MINUTES. NOW IT WAS ALMOST OVERHEAD. THE LIGHTNING FUELED GYER'S SENSE OF OCCASION.
RUN! GODZILLA!

THE LATE MOVIE WAS NEARING ITS CLIMAX, THE SOUND TURNED UP DEAFENINGLY LOUD. THE WHOLE SCENE STANK OF BOURBON AND DEPRAVITY. GYER MADE A NOTE OF IT FOR FUTURE USE IN THE PULPIT.

A CHILL BLEW IN FROM THE OFFICE. ALL THE WAY HERE HE'D HAD A SENSE OF BEING FOLLOWED, YET THERE WAS NOBODY ON HIS HEELS. HE CANCELLED HIS SUSPICIONS.

HIS BOMBAST AMAZED HER. SHE'D EXPECTED THIS SUBSPECIES TO BE EXTINCT BY NOW. COULD SUCH MELODRAMA BE CREDIBLE IN THIS SOPHISTICATED AGE?
SADIE HAD NEVER MUCH LIKED CHURCH PEOPLE, BUT THIS EXAMPLE WAS PARTICULARLY OFFEN-SIVE; THERE WAS MORE THAN A WHIFF OF MALICE BENEATH THE FLATULENCE.

HE WOULD NOT BE PLEASED WITH THE SCENE THAT AWAITED HIM IN LAURA MAY'S ROOM.
EARL?! EARL, ANSWER ME!
SADIE HAD ALREADY BEEN THERE. SHE HAD WATCHED THE LOVERS FOR A LITTLE WHILE, UNTIL THEIR PAS-SION BECAME TOO MUCH FOR HER AND HAD DRIVEN HER OUT TO COOL HERSELF BY WATCHING THE RAIN.

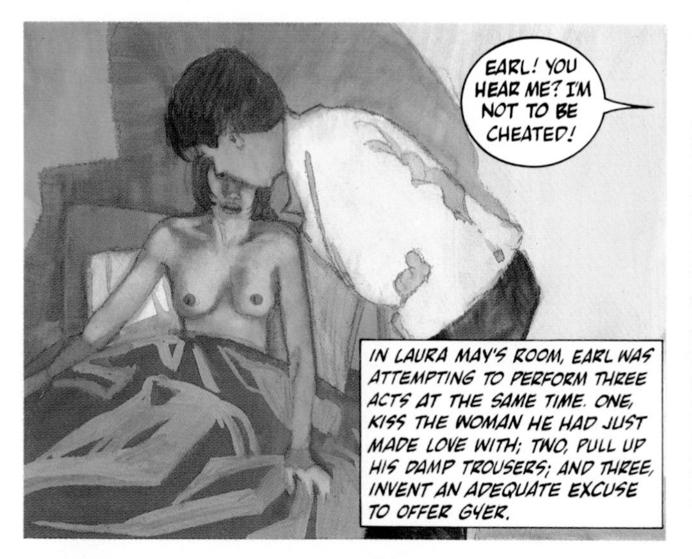
EARL! YOU HEAR ME? I'M NOT TO BE CHEATED!
IN LAURA MAY'S ROOM, EARL WAS ATTEMPTING TO PERFORM THREE ACTS AT THE SAME TIME. ONE, KISS THE WOMAN HE HAD JUST MADE LOVE WITH; TWO, PULL UP HIS DAMP TROUSERS; AND THREE, INVENT AN ADEQUATE EXCUSE TO OFFER GYER.

FOUND YOU!
EARL HAD HEARD TELL OF THE GREAT MAN'S RIGHTEOUS WRATH FROM VIRGINIA. FURNITURE HAD BEEN TRASHED, BONES BROKEN.

IS THERE NO END TO YOUR INIQUITY?
THIS ISN'T YOUR BUSINESS...
YOU GET OUT.

LET HIM BE! HE HASN'T DONE ANYTHING WRONG!
WHAT WOULD YOU KNOW ABOUT ERROR, WHORE?

THE BED DID STINK, BUT ONLY OF GOOD SOAP AND RECENT LOVE. SHE HAD NOTHING TO APOLOGIZE FOR, AND SHE WASN'T GOING TO LET THIS TWO BIT BIBLE-THUMPER INTIMIDATE HER.
I'LL CALL THE COPS! IF YOU DON'T LEAVE HIM ALONE, I'LL CALL THEM!

HOLD ON, EARL! I'LL GET HELP!
HER LOVER DIDN'T ANSWER.
SADIE WATCHED LAURA MAY, AND FOR THE FIRST TIME SINCE HER DEATH, SHE FELT A NOSTALGIA FOR CORPORALITY. IN PART BECAUSE SHE ENVIED HER BLISS WITH EARL, AND IN PART BECAUSE SADIE ITCHED TO HAVE A ROLE IN THE DRAMA THAT WAS RAPIDLY UNFOLDING AROUND HER.

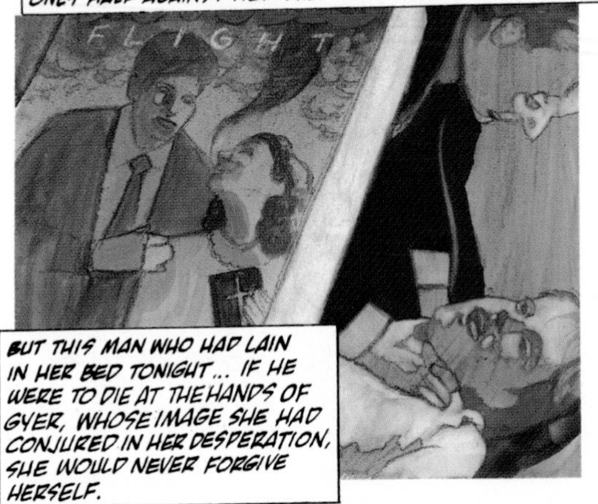
SOMETIMES, WHEN THE DAYS WERE LONG AND LONELY, LAURA MAY HAD DAYDREAMED DARK MEN LIKE THE EVANGELIST. SHE HAD IMAGINED THEM COMING BEFORE TORNADOES, WREATHED IN DUST. SHE HAD PICTURED HERSELF LIFTED UP BY THEM-- ONLY HALF AGAINST HER WILL--AND TAKEN AWAY.
BUT THIS MAN WHO HAD LAIN IN HER BED TONIGHT... IF HE WERE TO DIE AT THE HANDS OF GYER, WHOSE IMAGE SHE HAD CONJURED IN HER DESPERATION, SHE WOULD NEVER FORGIVE HERSELF.

WHAT'S GOING ON? WHAT YOU BEEN DOING, LAURA MAY?
NEVER MIND, PA. THERE'S NO TIME TO EXPLAIN.
BUT THERE'S MEN OUT THERE--
I KNOW. I KNOW. I WANT YOU TO CALL THE SHERIFF IN PANHANDLE. UNDERSTAND?

WHAT'S GOING ON?
NEVER MIND. JUST CALL ALVIN AND BE QUICK ABOUT IT OR WE'RE GOING TO HAVE ANOTHER MURDER ON OUR HANDS.
THE THOUGHT OF SLAUGHTER GALVANIZED MILTON CADE. HE AND LAURA MAY KNEW THAT, ON A NIGHT LIKE THIS, ALVIN BAKER AND HIS DEPUTY COULD BE A LONG TIME COMING.

IN THE MEANWHILE, GOD ALONE KNEW WHAT THE MAD-DOG PREACHER WOULD BE CAPABLE OF.

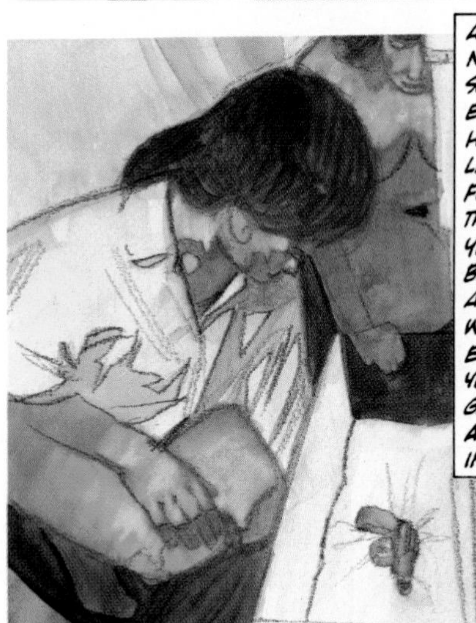
A THRILL OF RECOGNITION MADE SADIE'S SCALP TINGLE AS HER EYES ALIGHTED ON HER .38. SO IT WAS LAURA MAY WHO HAD FOUND THE GUN. THE WHEY-FACED SIX-YEAR-OLD WHO HAD BEEN RUNNING UP AND DOWN THE WALKWAY ALL THAT EVENING THIRTY YEARS AGO, PLAYING GAMES WITH HERSELF AND SINGING SONGS IN THE HOT STILL AIR.

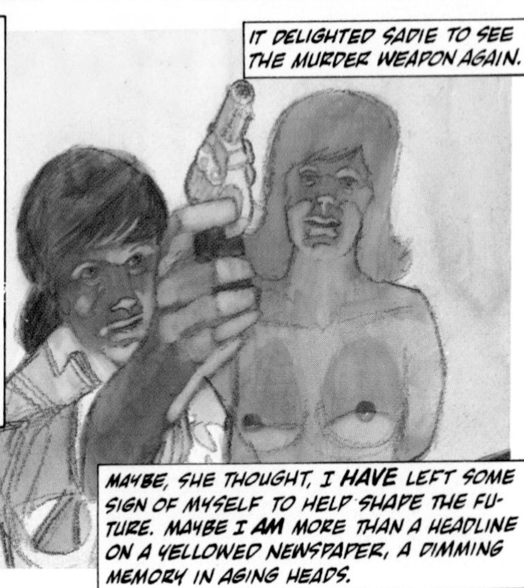
IT DELIGHTED SADIE TO SEE THE MURDER WEAPON AGAIN.
MAYBE, SHE THOUGHT, I HAVE LEFT SOME SIGN OF MYSELF TO HELP SHAPE THE FUTURE. MAYBE I AM MORE THAN A HEADLINE ON A YELLOWED NEWSPAPER, A DIMMING MEMORY IN AGING HEADS.

VIRGINIA LOOKED AT THE SEEDY FIGURE LEANING ON THE DOOR LINTEL ACROSS FROM HER.
SHE HAD LET THE DELUSION SHE HAD CONJURED HAVE WHAT WAY IT WOULD WITH HER. AND NEVER IN HER FORTY-ODD YEARS HAD SHE HEARD SUCH DEPRAVITY PROMISED.

BUT THOUGH THE SHADOW HAD COME AT HER AGAIN AND AGAIN, IT HAD FAILED TO CARRY ONE ACT OF VIOLATION THROUGH. THREE TIMES IT HAD TRIED. THREE TIMES THE URGENT WORDS, WHISPERED IN HER EAR HAD NOT BEEN REALIZED.
ITS FACE WAS CLEAR ENOUGH FOR HER TO READ THE BAFFLEMENT AND SHAME IN ITS FEATURES. IT VIEWED HER, SHE THOUGHT, WITH MURDER ON ITS MIND.

OUTSIDE, SHE HEARD HER HUSBAND'S VOICE ABOVE THE DIN OF THE THUNDER, AND EARL'S VOICE TOO, RAISED IN PROTEST. THERE WAS A FIERCE ARGUMENT GOING ON, THAT MUCH WAS APPARENT.
YOU FAILED.
YOU'RE JUST A DAMN DREAM OF MINE, AND YOU FAILED.

SHE DIDN'T UNDERSTAND WHY IT HADN'T EVAPORATED, BUT ITS FAILED RAPES LEFT IT BEREFT OF POWER OVER HER.
I'M LEAVING.
WHERE ARE YOU GOING?
OUT. TO HELP EARL.
NO, I HAVEN'T FINISHED WITH YOU.
YOU'RE JUST A PHANTOM. YOU CAN'T STOP ME.
I'M NO DELUSION, WOMAN. I'M BUCK DURNING. THIRTY YEARS AGO I WAS SHOT DEAD IN THIS VERY ROOM. JUST ABOUT WHERE YOU'RE STANDING, IN FACT.

"WE CAME BACK TONIGHT, SADIE AND I. A ONE NIGHT STAND AT THE SLAUGHTERHOUSE OF LOVE. THAT'S WHAT THEY CALLED THIS PLACE, DID YOU KNOW THAT?"

PEOPLE USED TO COME HERE FROM ALL OVER, JUST TO SEE WHERE SADIE DURNING SHOT HER HUSBAND BUCK. SICK PEOPLE, VIRGINIA, DON'T YOU THINK? MORE INTERESTED IN MURDER THAN LOVE. NOT ME...I'VE ALWAYS LIKED LOVE, YOU KNOW? ALMOST THE ONLY THING I'VE EVER HAD MUCH OF A TALENT FOR, IN FACT.
YOU LIED TO ME. YOU USED ME.

I HAVEN'T FINISHED YET. IN FACT I'VE BARELY STARTED.

BUT THIS TIME SHE WAS READY FOR HIM.

HE WASN'T GOING TO HUMILIATE HIMSELF WITH PURSUIT. SHE WOULD HAVE TO COME BACK, WOULDN'T SHE? IF SHE TOLD HER COMPANIONS WHAT SHE'D SEEN, THEY'D CALL HER CRAZY, MAYBE LOCK HER UP WHERE HE COULD HAVE HER ALL TO HIMSELF. NO, HE HAD A WINNER HERE.
I'LL BE WAITING! YOU HEAR ME, BITCH? I'LL BE WAITING!

SHE WOULD RETURN SOAKED TO THE SKIN, HER DRESS CLINGING TO HER IN A DOZEN FETCHING WAYS. PANICKY PERHAPS, TEARFUL, TOO WEAK TO RESIST HIS OVERTURES.
THEY'D MAKE MUSIC THEN. OH YES. UNTIL SHE BEGGED HIM TO STOP.

WHERE YOU GOING, LAURA MAY AND...JESUS! WHERE'D YOU GET THAT GODDAMN GUN?!

EARL?! WHERE ARE YOU? EARL?
Office

PEOPLE RUNNING AROUND LIKE CRAZIES...
WHO?
WHERE DID THEY GO?
ALL THIS YELLING. WE CAME HERE FOR SOME PRIVACY, FOR CHRIST'S SAKE.
THE CRAZIES!
SHE'S GOT A GUN! SEE THAT?

Office
THEY WENT AROUND THE BACK OF THE OFFICE!
EARL! ARE YOU THERE?
SADIE KEPT PACE WITH HER. THE CADE WOMAN HAD PLUCK, NO DOUBT OF THAT, BUT THERE WAS AN EDGE OF HYSTERIA IN HER VOICE WHICH SADIE DIDN'T LIKE TOO MUCH. THIS KIND OF BUSINESS (MURDER) REQUIRED DETACHMENT. PANIC WOULD ONLY CLOUD THE ISSUE; PASSION THE SAME.

WHY, WHEN SHE'D RAISED THAT .38 AND POINTED IT AT BUCK THERE'D BEEN NO ANGER TO SPOIL HER AIM, NOT A TRACE. IN THE FINAL ANALYSIS, THAT WAS WHY THEY'D SENT HER TO THE CHAIR. NOT FOR DOING IT, BUT FOR DOING IT TOO WELL.
BASTARD!
...EARL...
LAURA MAY WAS NOT SO COOL.

YOU'RE OUT OF YOUR MIND! LET ME GO!
ADMIT YOUR CRIME, SINNER!
DAMN YOU, NO!

YOU CAME TO DESTROY MY CRUSADE. ADMIT IT! ADMIT IT!
GO TO HELL!
CONFESS YOUR COMPLICITY, OR SO HELP ME I'LL BREAK EVERY BONE IN YOUR BODY!
EARL FOUGHT TO BE FREE OF GYER, BUT THE EVANGELIST WAS EASILY THE STRONGER OF THE TWO MEN.
PRAY! PRAY!

GET AWAY FROM HIM.
SADIE CALMLY NOTED THAT THE WOMAN'S AIM WAS NOT ALL IT COULD BE. EVEN IN CLEAR WEATHER SHE WAS PROBABLY NO SHARPSHOOTER. BUT HERE, UNDER STRESS, IN A DOWNPOUR, WHO BUT THE MOST EXPERIENCED MARKSMAN COULD GUARANTEE THE OUTCOME?
GYER LOOKED UP AT LAURA MAY. HE SHOWED NOT A FLICKER OF APPREHENSION.
HE'S MADE THE SAME CALCULATION I'VE JUST MADE. HE KNOWS DAMN WELL THE ODDS ARE AGAINST HIM GETTING HARMED.

THE WHORE!
DO YOU SEE HER, LORD? SEE HER SHAME, HER DEPRAVITY? MARK HER! SHE IS ONE OF THE COURT OF BABYLON!
I'M NO WHORE! DON'T YOU DARE CALL ME A WHORE!

PLEASE, LAURA MAY... GET OUT OF HERE. HE'S LOST HIS MIND.
IF YOU DON'T LET GO OF HIM...
YES? WHAT WILL YOU DO, WHORE?
I'LL SHOOT! I WILL! I'LL SHOOT!

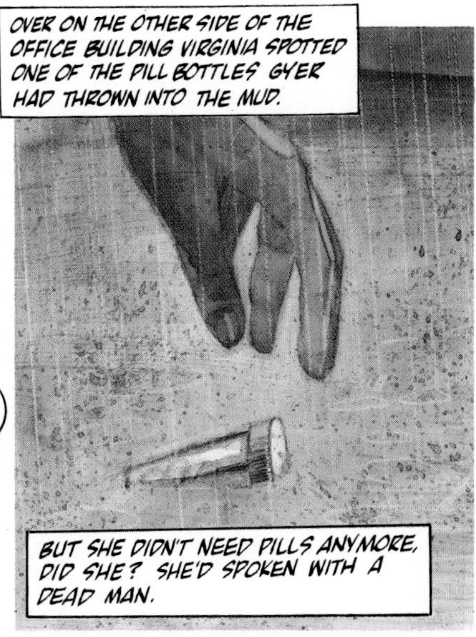
OVER ON THE OTHER SIDE OF THE OFFICE BUILDING VIRGINIA SPOTTED ONE OF THE PILL BOTTLES GYER HAD THROWN INTO THE MUD.
BUT SHE DIDN'T NEED PILLS ANYMORE, DID SHE? SHE'D SPOKEN WITH A DEAD MAN.

HER VERY TOUCH HAD MADE BUCK DURNING VISIBLE TO HER. WHAT A SKILL THAT WAS!
HER VISIONS WERE REAL, AND ALWAYS HAD BEEN; MORE TRUE THAN ALL THE SECONDHAND REVELATIONS HER PITIFUL HUSBAND COULD SPOUT. WHAT COULD PILLS DO BUT BEFUDDLE THIS NEWFOUND TALENT? LET THEM LIE.
HAS THERE BEEN AN ACCIDENT?
AS THE WORDS LEFT THE WOMAN'S LIPS...

BLAM
JOHN.
BEFORE THE ECHOES OF THE SHOT HAD DIED, SHE WAS MAKING HER WAY TOWARDS THEIR SOURCE, A PRAYER COMING AS SHE RAN. SHE PRAYED NOT THAT THE SCENARIO SHE HAD IMAGINED WAS WRONG, BUT RATHER THAT GOD WOULD FORGIVE HER FOR WILLING IT TRUE.

THE SCENE SHE FOUND ON THE OTHER SIDE OF THE BUILDING CONFOUNDED ALL HER EXPECTATIONS.
OH LORD, I THANK YOU...
EVEN AS VIRGINIA'S EYES SETTLED ON LAURA MAY, A FIGURE STEPPED THROUGH THE RAIN...

LAURA MAY CLEARLY DIDN'T UNDERSTAND HOW SHE'D DROPPED THE GUN. VIRGINIA KNEW. SHE COULD SEE THE PHANTOM, ALBEIT FLEETINGLY, AND SHE GUESSED ITS IDENTITY.

DON'T BE DEAD, EARL. I BEG YOU, DON'T BE DEAD!

MISSED ME BY A MILE.
...I THANK YOU FOR PRESERVING THIS, YOUR INSTRUMENT, IN HIS HOUR OF NEED...
VIRGINIA SHUT OUT THE IDIOT DRIVEL. THIS WAS THE MAN WHO HAD CONVINCED HER SO DEEPLY OF HER OWN DELUDED STATE THAT SHE'D GIVEN HERSELF TO BUCK DURNING.
WELL, **NO MORE**. SHE'D BEEN TERRORIZED ENOUGH. SHE'D SEEN SADIE ACT UPON THE REAL WORLD. SHE'D FELT BUCK DO THE SAME.
THE TIME WAS NOW RIPE TO REVERSE THE PROCEDURE.

IS THIS WISE?
VIRGINIA DIDN'T KNOW. WHAT WAS WISDOM ANYHOW? NOT THE STALE RHETORIC OF DEAD PROPHETS.

MAYBE WISDOM WAS LAURA MAY AND EARL EMBRACING IN THE MUD, CARELESS OF THE PRAYERS GYER WAS SPOUTING.
NOT BUCK? SURELY NOT.
HE ATTACKED ME.
YOU POOR LAMB.
I'M NO LAMB. NOT ANYMORE.

OR PERHAPS WISDOM WAS FINDING THE CANCER IN YOUR LIFE AND ROOTING IT OUT ONCE AND FOR ALL. GUN IN HAND, SHE HEADED BACK TO ROOM SEVEN.
REALIZING THAT THE WOMAN WAS PERFECTLY IN CHARGE OF HER DESTINY, SADIE HUNG BACK, FEARFUL THAT HER PRESENCE WOULD ALERT BUCK.

YOU CAME BACK.
I KNEW YOU WOULD.
THEY ALWAYS DO.
I WANT YOU TO SHOW YOURSELF--

I'M NAKED AS A BABE AS IT IS. WHAT DO YOU WANT ME TO DO, SKIN MYSELF? MIGHT BE FUN, AT THAT.
SHOW YOURSELF TO JOHN, MY HUSBAND. MAKE HIM SEE HIS ERROR.
OH, POOR JOHN. I DON'T THINK HE WANTS TO SEE ME, DO YOU?

HE THINKS I'M INSANE.

INSANITY CAN BE VERY USEFUL. THEY ALMOST SAVED SADIE FROM OLD SPARKY ON A PLEA OF INSANITY. BUT SHE WAS TOO HON-EST FOR HER OWN GOOD. SHE NEVER HAD MUCH SENSE.
BUT YOU...NOW, I THINK YOU KNOW WHAT'S BEST FOR YOU.
COME AND GET IT, VIRGINIA. GRUB'S UP.

NOT THIS TIME.

YOU CAN'T DO ME ANY HARM WITH THAT. I'M ALREADY DEAD, REMEMBER?
YOU HURT ME. WHY SHOULDN'T I BE ABLE TO HURT YOU BACK?
THE WAIL OF POLICE SIRENS ROSE FROM DOWN THE HIGHWAY.
WELL, WHAT DO YOU KNOW? SUCH A FUSS AND COMMOTION. WE BETTER GET DOWN TO SOME JAZZING, HONEY, BEFORE WE GET INTERRUPTED.

I WARN YOU, THIS IS SADIE'S GUN--
YOU WOULDN'T HURT ME. I KNOW YOU WOMEN. YOU SAY ONE THING AND YOU MEAN THE OPPOSITE.
AGAIN HE STEPPED TOWARD HER, LAUGHING.

DON'T.
IN THE INSTANT BEFORE SHE HEARD THE SOUND, AND FELT THE GUN LEAP IN HER HAND...
...SHE SAW JOHN APPEAR IN THE DOORWAY.

HAD HE BEEN THERE ALL ALONG, OR WAS HE COMING OUT OF THE RAIN, PRAYERS DONE, TO READ REVELATIONS TO HIS ERRING WIFE?
SHE WOULD NEVER KNOW.

SUDDENLY THERE WAS NOTHING IN ROOM SEVEN BUT VIRGINIA, HER DYING HUSBAND, AND THE SOUND OF THE RAIN.
NOW JOHN WOULD NEVER KNOW. THAT WAS THE PITY OF IT. HE COULD NEVER BE MADE TO CONCEDE HIS STUPIDITY AND RECANT HIS ARROGANCE.

NOT THIS SIDE OF THE GRAVE, ANYHOW. HE WAS SAFE, DAMN HIM, AND SHE WAS LEFT WITH A SMOKING GUN IN HER HAND.

PUT DOWN THE GUN AND COME OUT OF THERE!
THE VOICE FROM THE LOT SOUNDED HARSH AND UNCOMPROMISING.
VIRGINIA DIDN'T ANSWER.
YOU HEAR ME, IN THERE? THIS IS SHERIFF BAKER. THE PLACE IS SURROUNDED, SO COME OUT, OR YOU'RE DEAD.

THEY WOULDN'T EXECUTE HER FOR WHAT SHE'D DONE, THE WAY THEY HAD SADIE. BUT SHE'D BE IN PRISON FOR A LONG TIME, AND SHE WAS TIRED OF REGIMES.
BETTER TO FINISH HERE.
IS THAT WISE?
THEY'LL LOCK ME AWAY. I COULDN'T FACE THAT.

TRUE. THEY'LL PUT YOU BEHIND BARS. BUT IT WON'T BE FOR LONG.
YOU MUST BE JOKING. I JUST SHOT MY HUSBAND IN COLD BLOOD.
YOU DIDN'T MEAN TO. YOU WERE AIMING AT BUCK.
WAS I? I WONDER.

YOU CAN PLEAD INSANITY, THE WAY I SHOULD HAVE DONE.
WHEN YOU'RE SET FREE, YOU'LL BE NOTORIOUS. THAT'S WORTH LIVING FOR, ISN'T IT?
VIRGINIA HADN'T THOUGHT OF THAT.

YOU'VE GOT TEN SECONDS, LADY, AND I MEAN TEN.
I CAN'T FACE THE HUMILIATION.
PITY. THE RAIN'S CLEARING. THERE'S A MOON.
A MOON? REALLY?
5... 6...
YOU HAVE TO MAKE UP YOUR MIND. THEY'LL SHOOT YOU GIVEN HALF THE CHANCE.

STOP!
GOOD. I'M SO PLEASED.
BAKER STOPPED COUNTING.

I CAN'T GO ALONE.
NO NEED.

PUT YOUR HANDS UP WHERE I CAN SEE THEM!
LOOK, LOOK UP!
WHY'D YOU KILL HIM?!
THE MOON WAS THERE, WIDE AND WHITE.

VIRGINIA GAVE THEM THE CRAZIEST SMILE SHE COULD MUSTER.
THE DEVIL MADE ME DO IT.

THE END

WHY COULD VANESSA NEVER RESIST THE ROAD THAT HAD NO SIGNPOST MARKING IT, THE TRACK THAT LED TO GOD ALONE KNEW WHERE?

HER ENTHUSIASM FOR FOLLOWING HER NOSE HAD GOT HER INTO TROUBLE OFTEN ENOUGH IN THE PAST. A NEAR-FATAL NIGHT SPENT LOST IN THE ALPS; THAT EPISODE IN MARRAKECH THAT HAD ALMOST ENDED IN RAPE; THE ADVENTURE WITH THE SWORD-SWALLOWER'S APPRENTICE IN THE WILDS OF LOWER MANHATTAN.

AND YET DESPITE WHAT BITTER EXPERIENCE SHOULD HAVE TAUGHT HER, WHEN THE CHOICE LAY BETWEEN THE MARKED ROUTE AND THE UNMARKED, SHE WOULD ALWAYS, WITHOUT QUESTION, TAKE THE LATTER.

HERE, FOR INSTANCE. THIS ROAD THAT MEANDERED TOWARD THE COAST OF KITHNOS: WHAT COULD IT POSSIBLY OFFER HER BUT AN UNEVENTFUL DRIVE THROUGH THE SCRUBLAND HEREABOUTS -- A CHANCE ENCOUNTER WITH A GOAT ALONG THE WAY -- AND A VIEW FROM THE CLIFFS OF THE BLUE AEGEAN.

BUT THE OTHER HIGHWAYS THAT LED FROM THIS CROSSROADS WERE SO CLEARLY **MARKED**: ONE TO LOUTRA, WITH ITS RUINED VENETIAN FORT, THE OTHER TO DRIOPIS. SHE HAD VISITED NEITHER VILLAGE, BUT THE FACT THAT THEY WERE SO CLEARLY NAMED SERIOUSLY MARRED THEIR ATTRACTION FOR HER.

THIS OTHER ROAD, HOWEVER, THOUGH IT MIGHT -- INDEED PROBABLY ***DID*** -- LEAD NOWHERE, AT LEAST LED TO AN ***UNNAMED*** NOWHERE. THAT WAS NO SMALL RECOMMENDATION. THUS FUELED BY SHEER PERVERSITY, SHE SET OFF ALONG IT.

THE SOUND OF GUNS WAS NOT PARTICULARLY PLEASANT, BUT COULD SHE POSSIBLY TURN HER BACK ON SUCH A MYSTERY?

DISTANCES WERE DECEPTIVE IN SUCH UNREMARKABLE TERRAIN; ONE SANDY HILLOCK LOOKED MUCH LIKE THE NEXT. SHE PICKED HER WAY AMONG THE SQUIRTING CUCUMBER FOR FULLY TEN MINUTES BEFORE SHE BECAME CERTAIN THAT SHE HAD MISSED THE SPOT FROM WHICH PURSUED AND PURSUER HAD VANISHED--
--AND BY THAT TIME SHE WAS LOST IN A SEA OF GRASS-CRESTED KNOLLS. THE CRIES HAD LONG SINCE CEASED, THE SHOTS TOO. SHE WAS LEFT ONLY WITH THE SOUND OF GULLS, AND THE RASPING DEBATE OF CICADAS AROUND HER FEET.
DAMN. WHY DO I DO THESE THINGS?
SHE SELECTED THE LARGEST HILLOCK IN THE VINICITY AND TRUDGED UP ITS FLANK, HER FEET UNCERTAIN IN THE SANDY SOIL, TO SEE IF THE VANTAGE POINT OFFERED A VIEW OF THE TRACK SHE'D LEFT, OR EVEN OF THE SEA.
ALL THAT WAS REVEALED AT THE SUMMIT WAS THE EXTENT OF HER OWN ISOLATION.
THE BREEZE WOULD MOST LIKELY BE OFF THE SEA, AND SHE REASONED THAT SHE MIGHT USE THAT SLENDER INFORMATION TO BASE HER MENTAL CARTOGRAPHY UPON.

BABEL'S CHILDREN

HER PERVERSITY UNCHASTENED BY ADVENTURE, SHE FOLLOWED THE WALKWAY THAT LOOKED LEAST PROMISING...
...AND IT LED HER OUT OF THE SUN AND INTO A BALMY PASSAGE.
THE YARD BELOW WAS MOTTLED WITH DOVE'S DROPPINGS: SEVERAL OF THE CULPRITS SAT IN A MYRTLE TREE AND COOED AT HER APPEARANCE.
NOW, THE PIECES OF THIS MYSTERY FELL INTO PLACE: THE SECLUDED LOCATION, THE SILENCE, THE PLAINNESS OF THE YARDS AND WALKWAYS-- THIS WAS SURELY A RELIGIOUS ESTABLISHMENT.

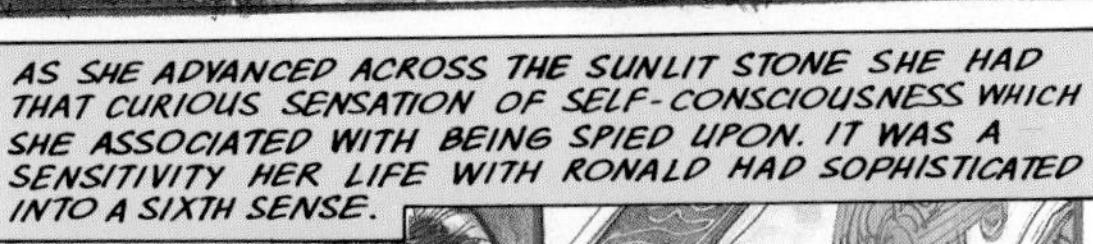
SHE HAD BEEN GODLESS SINCE EARLY ADOLESCENCE AND HAD SELDOM STEPPED OVER THE THRESHOLD OF A CHURCH IN THE INTERVENING TWENTY-FIVE YEARS. NOW, AT FORTY-ONE, SHE WAS PAST RECALL, AND SO FELT DOUBLY A TRESPASSER HERE.
BUT THEN, SHE WASN'T SEEKING SANCTUARY, WAS SHE? MERELY DIRECTIONS. SHE COULD ASK THEM AND GET GONE.

AS SHE ADVANCED ACROSS THE SUNLIT STONE SHE HAD THAT CURIOUS SENSATION OF SELF-CONSCIOUSNESS WHICH SHE ASSOCIATED WITH BEING SPIED UPON. IT WAS A SENSITIVITY HER LIFE WITH RONALD HAD SOPHISTICATED INTO A SIXTH SENSE.
HIS RIDICULOUS JEALOUSIES, WHICH HAD, ONLY THREE MONTHS EARLIER, ENDED THEIR MARRIAGE, HAD LED HIM TO SPYING STRATEGIES THAT WOULD NOT HAVE SHAMED THE AGENCIES OF WHITEHALL OR WASHINGTON. NOW SHE FELT NOT ONE BUT SEVERAL PAIRS OF EYES UPON HER.

NOBODY MADE ANY EFFORT TO CALL DOWN TO HER, HOWEVER. A MUTE ORDER, PERHAPS, THEIR VOW OF SILENCE SO PROFOUNDLY OBSERVED THAT SHE WOULD HAVE TO COMMUNICATE IN SIGN LANGUAGE? WELL, SO BE IT.

THEN SHE HEARD RUNNING FEET-- SEVERAL PAIRS, RUSHING TOWARD HER-- AND THE SOUND OF THE IRON GATES CLANGING CLOSED. FOR SOME REASON HER HEARTBEAT TRIPPED OVER ITSELF AND ALARMED HER BLOOD. STARTLED, IT LEAPED TO HER FACE AS HER EXHAUSTED LEGS BEGAN TO QUIVER.
TAPTAPTAPTAP
SHE STOOD STOCK STILL; BEST NOT TO RUN, SHE THOUGHT, WITH OUR LADY AT YOUR BACK.
SHE TURNED TO FACE THE OWNERS OF THOSE URGENT FOOTSTEPS AND AS SHE DID SO CAUGHT SIGHT OF THE STONE VIRGIN'S HEAD MOVING A FRACTION. ITS BLUE EYES HAD FOLLOWED HER ACROSS THE YARD AND NOW WERE UNMISTAKABLY FOLLOWING HER BACK.
THERE WAS NO WORD OF EXPLANATION OFFERED, BUT THEN IN A PLACE THAT HARBORED ARMED MEN DRESSED AS NUNS A GLIMPSE OF SWEET REASON WAS DOUBTLESS AS RARE AS FEATHERED FROGS.
TO QUENCH HER THIRST DURING HER INCARCERATION, ONE OF THE NUNS HAD PROVIDED A BOTTLE OF PALATABLE RETSINA, AND, TO COMPLETE THIS CATALOGUE OF INCONGRUITIES, THE BEST DEEP-DISH PIZZA SHE'D HAD THIS SIDE OF CHICAGO. ALICE, LOST IN WONDERLAND, COULD NOT HAVE THOUGHT IT CURIOUSER.

THERE MAY HAVE BEEN AN ERROR.
THE CONCESSION CAME AFTER SEVERAL HOURS OF INTERROGATION BY THE MAN, WHO CLAIMED HIS NAME WAS MR. KLEIN. BENEATH HIS CALCULATED ENGLISH, VANESSA THOUGHT SHE SNIFFED THE HINT OF AN ACCENT. FRENCH? GERMAN? IT WAS ONLY WHEN HE PRODUCED SOME CHOCOLATE FROM HIS DESK THAT SHE DECIDED HE WAS SWISS.

AN ERROR? YOU'RE DAMN RIGHT THERE'S BEEN AN ERROR!
WE'VE LOCATED YOUR CAR. WE HAVE ALSO CHECKED WITH YOUR HOTEL. SO FAR, YOUR STORY HAS BEEN VERIFIED.
WELL, I'M GLAD YOU'RE SATISFIED. NOW WILL YOU LET ME GET BACK TO MY HOTEL?! I'M TIRED.
I'M AFRAID THAT WON'T BE POSSIBLE.

LOOK HERE, YOU...

IT'S ALL RIGH, STANISLAUS. MRS. JAPE HASN'T SLIT MY THROAT.
TRUNK!

WHY?
WHY WHAT?
THE NUNS.
SLAM

IN MY OWN OPINION, MUCH OF THIS IS REDUNDANT, MRS. JAPE, AND YOU HAVE MY PERSONAL ASSURANCE THAT I WILL SEE YOU RELEASED AS RAPIDLY AS IS HUMANLY POSSIBLE. IN THE MEANWHILE I BEG YOUR INDULGENCE.
THINK OF IT AS A GAME. THEY LIKE GAMES.
WHO DO?
NEVER MIND. THE LESS YOU KNOW, THE LESS WE'LL HAVE TO MAKE YOU FORGET.
NONE OF THIS MAKES ANY SENSE.
NOR SHOULD IT. YOU MADE A REGRETTABLE ERROR IN COMING HERE, MRS. JAPE. AND INDEED, WE MADE AN ERROR LETTING YOU IN. NORMALLY, OUR DEFENSES ARE STRICTER THAN YOU FOUND THEM. BUT YOU CAUGHT US OFF-GUARD... AND THE NEXT THING WE KNEW--
LOOK, I DON'T KNOW THAT'S GOING ON HERE. I DON'T WANT TO KNOW. ALL I WANT IS TO BE ALLOWED TO GO BACK TO MY HOTEL AND FINISH MY HOLIDAY IN PEACE.
IS THAT SO MUCH TO ASK? I HAVEN'T DONE ANYTHING, I HAVEN'T SEEN ANYTHING. WHAT'S THE PROBLEM?
THE PROBLEM-- NOW THERE'S A QUESTION.
STANISLAUS?
I SHALL PROTEST TO MY EMBASSY! I HAVE RIGHTS!
PLEASE. SHOUTING WILL HELP NONE OF US.
SHALL WE GO?
DO I HAVE ANY CHOICE?
NO.
THE TRICK OF GOOD FARCE, SHE HAD ONCE BEEN INFORMED BY HER BROTHER-IN-LAW, A SOMETIME ACTOR, WAS THAT IT BE PLAYED WITH DEADLY SERIOUSNESS. THERE SHOULD BE NO SLY WINKS TO THE GALLERY, SIGNALING THE FARCEUR'S COMIC INTENTION; NO BUSINESS THAT WAS SO OUTRAGEOUS IT WOULD UNDERMINE THE REALITY OF THE PIECE. BY THESE STRINGENT STANDARDS SHE WAS SURROUNDED BY A CAST OF EXPERTS: ALL WILLING-- HABITS, WIMPLES AND SPYING MADONNAS NOTWITHSTANDING -- TO PERFORM AS THOUGH THIS RIDICULOUS SITUATION WAS IN NO WAY OUT OF THE ORDINARY.

SHE SLEPT WELL, HELPED ON HER WAY BY HALF THE CONTENTS OF A BOTTLE OF WHISKEY THAT SOME THOUGHTFUL PERSON HAD LEFT IN HER LITTLE ROOM WHEN SHE RETURNED TO IT.
MRS. JAPE... MRS. JAPE, MAY WE HAVE WORDS?
WHO ARE YOU?
HER HEAD FELT SWOLLEN, HER TONGUE LIKE A SUEDE GLOVE. THE OLD MAN'S BREATH WAS TWO PARTS STALE OUZO TO ONE OF FRESH AIR. IT KEPT HER FROM PRESSING TOO CLOSE TO THE WINDOW, THOUGH HE BECKONED HER.
AN ADMIRER.
DO I KNOW YOU?
YOU'RE MUCH TOO YOUNG. BUT I KNOW YOU. I WATCHED YOU COME IN. I WANTED TO WARN YOU, BUT I DIDN'T HAVE TIME.
THE FEATURES, SUNBURNED AND LEATHERY, REMINDED HER OF SOMEBODY.
ARE YOU A PRISONER HERE TOO?
IN A MANNER OF SPEAKING. TELL ME... DID YOU SEE FLOYD? HE ESCAPED. THE DAY BEFORE YESTERDAY.
OH. FLOYD WAS THE MAN THEY WERE CHASING?
YES. HE SLIPPED OUT, YOU SEE. THEY WENT AFTER-- THE CLODS-- AND LEFT THE GATE OPEN. THE SECURITY IS SHOCKING THESE DAYS-- NOT THAT I'M NOT PLEASED YOU'RE HERE...
THERE WAS SOME DESPERATION IN HIS EYES, SHE THOUGHT; SOME SORROW HE FOUGHT TO KEEP SUBMERGED.
WE HEARD SHOTS. THEY... THEY DIDN'T GET HIM, DID THEY?
NOT THAT I SAW. I WENT TO LOOK. BUT THERE WAS NO SIGN--
HA! MAYBE HE DID GET AWAY THEN.
IT HAD ALREADY OCCURRED TO VANESSA THAT THIS CONVERSATION MIGHT BE A TRAP; THAT THE OLD MAN WAS HER CAPTOR'S DUPE, AND THIS WAS JUST ANOTHER WAY TO SQUEEZE INFORMATION FROM HER. BUT HER INSTINCTS INSTRUCTED HER OTHERWISE.
HE LOOKED AT HER WITH SUCH AFFECTION, AND HIS FACE, WHICH WAS THAT OF A MASTER CLOWN, SEEMED INCAPABLE OF FORGED FEELING. FOR BETTER OR WORSE, SHE TRUSTED HIM. SHE HAD LITTLE CHOICE.
HELP ME GET OUT. I HAVE TO GET OUT.

SO SOON? YOU ONLY JUST ARRIVED.
I'M NOT A THIEF. I DON'T LIKE BEING LOCKED UP.
OF COURSE YOU DON'T. I'M SORRY. IT'S JUST THAT A BEAUTIFUL WOMAN... I NEVER HAD MUCH OF A WAY WITH WORDS...
ARE YOU SURE I DON'T KNOW YOU FROM SOMEWHERE? YOUR FACE IS SOMEHOW FAMILIAR.
ALL?
REALLY? THAT'S VERY NICE. WE ALL THINK WE'RE FORGOTTEN HERE, YOU SEE.
WE WERE SNATCHED AWAY SUCH A TIME AGO. MANY OF US WERE ONLY BEGINNING OUR RESEARCHES. THAT'S WHY FLOYD MADE A RUN FOR IT. HE WANTED TO DO A FEW MONTH'S DECENT WORK BEFORE THE END. I FEEL THE SAME SOMETIMES.
MY NAME IS HARVEY GOMM... PROFESSOR HARVEY GOMM...THOUGH THESE DAYS I FORGET WHAT I WAS PROFESSOR OF.
YOU DON'T REMEMBER, DO YOU?
IT WAS A SINGULAR NAME, AND IT RANG BELLS, BUT VANESSA COULD AT PRESENT FIND NO TUNE IN THE CHIMES.
SHE WISHED SHE COULD LIE, BUT THAT MIGHT ALIENATE THE MAN--THE ONLY VOICE OF SANITY SHE'D DISCOVERED HERE--MORE THAN THE TRUTH.
NO... I DON'T EXACTLY REMEMBER. MAYBE A CLUE?
SOMEONE'S COMING! CAN'T TALK NOW, MRS. JAPE.
CALL ME VANESSA.
MAY I? VANESSA.
YOU WILL HELP ME?
AS BEST I MAY. BUT IF YOU SEE ME IN COMPANY--
WE NEVER MET.
PRECISELY. AU REVOIR.
WHEN HER CUSTODIAN, AN AMIABLE THUG CALLED GUILLEMOT, ARRIVED SEVERAL MINUTES LATER, SHE WAS ALL SMILES.
WHEN YOU'RE DONE, I'LL ESCORT YOU TO MR. KLEIN.
YOU MEAN HE DOESN'T WANT THE PLEASURE OF MY COMPANY FOR BREAKFAST?

HER OUTBURST OF THE PREVIOUS DAY SEEMED TO HAVE BORNE SOME FRUIT.
WE HAVE DECIDED TO GIVE YOU THE RUN OF THE GROUNDS-- WITH GUILLEMOT IN ATTENDANCE, OF COURSE. WE DON'T WANT YOUR STAY HERE TO BE UNPLEASANT... PERHAPS SOME SUN WILL IMPROVE YOUR DISPOSITION.
PERHAPS... AND A CHANGE OF CLOTHES AS WELL-- WHY, MR. KLEIN, YOU ARE ALL HEART!
BUT THE CLOTHES AND NEW FREEDOMS WERE A WARNING FLAG TO VANESSA: RELEASE WAS NOT TO BE SWIFTLY FORTHCOMING. HOW LONG WOULD IT BE, SHE TRIED TO CALCULATE, BEFORE THE RATHER OBTUSE MANAGER OF HER TINY HOTEL REALIZED THAT SHE WASN'T COMING BACK-- AND IN THAT EVENT, WHAT WOULD HE DO?
PERHAPS HE HAD ALREADY ALERTED THE AUTHORITIES; PERHAPS THEY WOULD FIND THE ABANDONED CAR AND TRACE HER TO THIS CURIOUS FORTRESS. ON THIS LAST POINT HER HOPES WERE DASHED THAT VERY MORNING, DURING HER CONSTITUTIONAL...
HER CAPTORS WERE NOT FOOLS. SHE MIGHT HAVE TO WAIT UNTIL SOMEBODY BACK IN ENGLAND BECAME CONCERNED AND ATTEMPTED TO TRACE HER WHEREABOUTS, DURING WHICH TIME SHE MIGHT WELL DIE OF BOREDOM.
NO, SAMUEL IS MINE, I TELL YOU!
OTHERS IN THE PLACE HAD FOUND DIVERSIONS TO KEEP THEM FROM INSANITY'S DOOR. VANESSA COULD DISTINCTLY HEAR VOICES-- ONE OF THEM GOMM'S-- FROM A NEARBY COURTYARD. THEY WERE RAISED IN EXCITEMENT.
WHAT'S GOING ON?
THEY'RE PLAYING GAMES.
CAN WE GO AND WATCH?
NO.
GO, YOU SILLY THING!
SAMUEL, NO SITTING!
C'MON! YOU'RE ALMOST THERE!
FROGS. THEY'RE RACING FROGS.
I WONDERED.
BETTER NOT.
DESPITE GUILLEMOT'S ADVICE, ONCE HER ATTENTION FOCUSED ON THE SOUND OF THE GAMES SHE COULD NOT DRIVE THE DIN FROM HER HEAD. IT CONTINUED TROUGHOUT THE AFTERNOON, RISING AND FALLING. SOMETIMES LAUGHTER WOULD ERUPT; AS OFTEN, THERE WOULD BE ARGUMENTS. THEY WERE LIKE CHILDREN, GOMM AND HIS FRIENDS, THE WAY THEY FOUGHT OVER SUCH AN INCONSEQUENTIAL PURSUIT AS RACING FROGS. BUT IN LIEU OF MORE NOURISHING DIVERSIONS, COULD SHE BLAME THEM?

I HEARD YOU THIS MORNING, IN ONE OF THE COURTYARDS. AND THEN THIS AFTERNOON, TOO. YOU SEEMED TO BE HAVING A GOOD DEAL OF FUN.
OH, THE GAMES. IT WAS A BUSY DAY. SO MUCH TO BE SORTED OUT.
DO YOU THINK YOU COULD PERSUADE THEM TO LET ME JOIN YOU? I'M GETTING SO BORED IN HERE.
POOR VANESSA. I WISH I COULD HELP. BUT IT'S PRACTICALLY IMPOSSIBLE. WE'RE SO OVERWORKED AT THE MOMENT, ESPECIALLY WITH FLOYD'S ESCAPE.
OVERWORKED, SHE THOUGHT, RACING FROGS? FEARING TO OFFEND, SHE DIDN'T VOICE THE DOUBT.
WHAT'S GOING ON HERE? YOU'RE NOT CRIMINALS, ARE YOU?
CRIMINALS?
I'M SORRY...
I SUPPOSE IT MUST STRIKE YOU AS OFF... OUR BEING LOCKED UP HERE. BUT NO, WE'RE NOT CRIMINALS.
WHAT THEN? WHAT'S THE BIG SECRET?
IF I TELL YOU, WILL YOU HELP US TO GET OUT OF HERE?
HOW?
YOUR CAR. IT'S AT THE FRONT.
YES, I SAW IT.
IF WE COULD GET TO IT, WOULD YOU DRIVE US?
HOW MANY OF YOU?
FOUR. THERE'S ME, THERE'S IRENIYA, THERE'S MOTTERSHEAD, AND GOLDBERG. OF COURSE, FLOYD'S PROBABLY OUT THERE SOMEWHERE, BUT HE'LL JUST HAVE TO LOOK AFTER HIMSELF, WON'T HE?
IT'S A SMALL CAR.
WE'RE SMALL PEOPLE. YOU SHRINK WITH AGE, YOU KNOW, LIKE DRIED FRUIT. AND WE'RE OLD. WITH FLOYD WE HAD THREE HUNDRED AND NINETY-EIGHT YEARS BETWEEN US.
ALL THAT BITTER EXPERIENCE, AND NOT ONE OF US WISE.

THEY FOUND HIM. OH MY GOD, THEY FOUND HIM. GOODBYE...!
WE GOT FLOYD! CALL MR. KLEIN!
I HOPE THAT MAN CHOKES ON HIS NEXT PIECE OF CHOCOLATE...
VANESSA COULD NOT CATCH MORE THAN ONE IN EVERY TEN WORDS, BUT THE VERBAL ASSAULT RAPIDLY REDUCED THE OLD MAN TO TEARS.
SO FAR, HER TIME HERE HAD BROUGHT A CURIOUS COLLECTION OF EXPERIENCES: ONE MOMENT PLEASANT (GOMM'S SMILE, THE PIZZA, THE SOUND OF GAMES PLAYED IN A SIMILAR COURTYARD), THE NEXT (THE INTERROGATION, THE BULLYING SHE'D JUST WITNESSED) UNPALATABLE...
...AND YET SHE STILL WAS NO NEARER TO UNDERSTANDING WHAT THE FUNCTION OF THIS PRISON WAS: WHY IT ONLY HAD FIVE INMATES (SIX, IF SHE INCLUDED HERSELF) AND ALL SO OLD--SHRUNK BY AGE, GOMM HAD SAID. BUT AFTER KLEIN'S HUMILIATION OF FLOYD SHE WAS NOW CERTAIN THAT NO SECRET, HOWEVER PRESSING, WOULD KEEP HER FROM AIDING GOMM IN HIS BID FOR FREEDOM.

THE PROFESSOR DID NOT COME BACK THAT EVENING, WHICH DISAPPOINTED HER. PERHAPS FLOYD'S RECAPTURE HAD MEANT STRICTER REGULATIONS ABOUT THE PLACE, SHE REASONED, THOUGH THAT PRINCIPLE SCARCELY APPLIED TO HER. SHE, IT SEEMED, WAS PRACTICALLY FORGOTTEN.
THOUGH GUILLEMOT BROUGHT HER FOOD AND DRINK HE DID NOT STAY TO TEACH HER POKER AS THEY HAD ARRANGED, NOR WAS SHE ESCORTED OUT TO TAKE THE AIR.
LEFT IN THE STUFFY ROOM WITHOUT COMPANY, HER MIND UNDISTURBED BY ANY ENTERTAINMENT BUT COUNTING HER TOES, SHE RAPIDLY BECAME LISTLESS AND SLEEPY.
LATIN WAS NOT HER FORTE; SHE HOPED THE FINAL WORDS WERE AN ENDEARMENT, NOT AN INSTRUCTION.
VANESSA, be ready
Yours,
in saecula saeculorum
H.G
CLEARLY GOMM DIDN'T INTEND HER TO USE IT NOW, HOWEVER, BUT TO WAIT FOR SOME SIGNAL. BE READY, HE'D WRITTEN. EASIER SAID THAN DONE, OF COURSE.
IT WAS SO TEMPTING, WITH THE DOOR OPEN AND THE PASSAGEWAY OUT TO THE SUN CLEAR, TO FORGET GOMM AND THE OTHERS AND MAKE A BREAK FOR IT. BUT H.G. HAD DOUBTLESS TAKEN SOME RISK ACQUIRING THE KEY. SHE OWED HIM HER ALLEGIANCE.
BUT GOMM'S CALL DIDN'T COME. THE AFTERNOON DRAGGED ON INTO EVENING. GUILLEMOT APPEARED WITH ANOTHER PIZZA AND A CAN OF COCA-COLA FOR DINNER, AND BEFORE SHE KNEW IT NIGHT HAD FALLEN AND ANOTHER DAY WAS GONE.
SOMETIME AFTER MIDNIGHT SHE DECIDED THAT WAITING HERE FOR THE AXE TO FALL WAS NOT HER STYLE AT ALL, AND SHE WOULD BE WISE TO DO AS FLOYD HAD DONE, AND RUN FOR IT.
PERHAPS THEY WOULD COME BY COVER OF DARKNESS, SHE THOUGHT, BUT THEY DIDN'T. THE MOON ROSE, IT SEAS SMIRKING, AND THERE WAS STILL NO SIGN OF H.G. OR THIS PROMISED EXODUS.

A LIGHT BREEZE TEASED THE LEAVES OF TWO ENTWINED LAUREL-TREES IN THE CENTER OF THE YARD; NIGHT INSECTS TUNED UP IN THE WALLS.

PEACEABLE AS IT WAS, THE SQUARE OFFERED NO PROMISING ROUTE THAT SHE COULD SEE, AND SHE WAS ABOUT TO GO BACK THE WAY SHE'D COME WHEN THE MOON SHOOK OFF ITS VEILS...

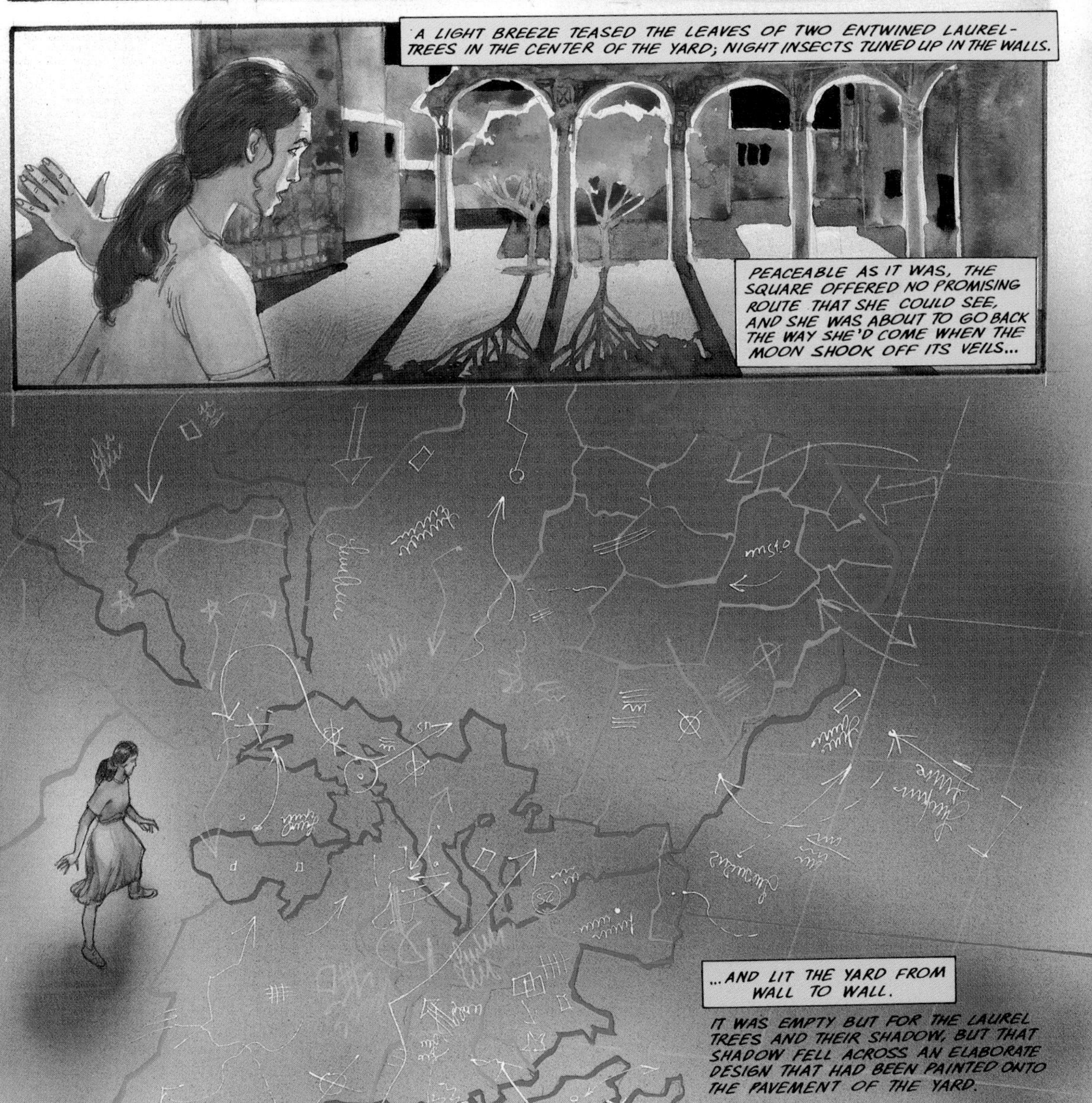

SHE STARED AT IT, TOO CURIOUS TO RETREAT, THOUGH SHE COULD MAKE NO SENSE OF THE THING AT FIRST; THE PATTERN SEEMED TO BE JUST THAT: A PATTERN. THEN IT DAWNED ON HER THAT SHE WAS VIEWING THE ENTIRE PICTURE UPSIDE DOWN.
THOUGH MANY OF THE SYMBOLS WERE IDIOSYNCRATIC, IT WAS CLEAR THAT THE MAP WAS RIFE WITH POLITICAL DETAIL. CONTESTED BORDERS, TERRITORIAL WATERS, EXCLUSION ZONES. MANY OF THESE HAD BEEN DRAWN AND REDRAWN IN CHALK, AS IF IN RESPONSE TO DAILY INTELLIGENCE.
IN SOME REGIONS, WHERE EVENTS WERE PARTICULARLY FRAUGHT, THE LAND MASS WAS ALL BUT OBSCURED BY SCRIBBLING. SHE DIDN'T HEAR THE FOOTSTEPS AT THE NORTH POLE UNTIL THEIR OWNER WAS STEPPING OUT OF HIDING AND INTO THE MOONLIGHT.
WHAT ARE YOU DOING HERE?

I COULDN'T GO ON WAITING, HARVEY. THIS IS NO PLACE TO TAKE A HOLIDAY.
YOU'RE RIGHT, OF COURSE.
IT'S HOPELESS. HOPELESS. YOU SHOULD MAKE YOUR GETAWAY ON YOUR OWN. FORGET ABOUT US. THEY'LL NEVER LET US OUT. THE TRUTH'S TOO TERRIBLE.
WHAT TRUTH?
FORGET ABOUT IT. FORGET WE EVER MET.
I WILL NOT. I HAVE TO KNOW WHAT'S HAPPENING HERE.
PERHAPS YOU SHOULD KNOW. PERHAPS THE WHOLE WORLD SHOULD KNOW.
WHAT'S THE MAP FOR?
THIS IS WHERE WE PLAY.
OF COURSE, IT WASN'T ALWAYS GAMES. BUT SYSTEMS DECAY, YOU KNOW. IT'S AN IRREFUTABLE CONDITION COMMON TO BOTH MATTER AND IDEAS. YOU START OFF WITH FINE INTENTIONS AND IN TWO DECADES... TWO DECADES... WE'RE PLAYING WITH FROGS.
YOU'RE NOT MAKING MUCH SENSE, HARVEY. ARE YOU DELIBERATELY OBTUSE OR IS THIS SENILITY?
THERE WAS A DAY OF SANITY, BACK IN 1962, IN WHICH IT OCCURRED TO THE POTENTATES THAT THEY WERE ON THE VERGE OF DESTROYING THE WORLD. IF ANNIHILATION WAS TO BE PREVENTED, THEY DECIDED, OUR BETTER INSTINCTS HAD TO PREVAIL. THE MIGHTY GATHERED BEHIND LOCKED DOORS AT A SYMPOSIUM IN GENEVA, THE LEADERS OF POLITIBUROS AND PARLIAMENTS, CONGRESSES, SENATES -- THE LORDS OF THE EARTH -- IN ONE COLOSSAL DEBATE.
AND IT WAS DECIDED THAT IN THE FUTURE WORLD AFFAIRS SHOULD BE OVERSEEN BY A SPECIAL COMMITTEE, MADE UP OF GREAT AND INFLUENTIAL MINDS LIKE MY OWN, AND INTELLECTUAL AND MORAL ELITE, WHOSE COLLECTIVE WISDOM WOULD BRING A NEW GOLDEN AGE. THAT WAS THE THEORY ANYWAY.
AND FOR A WHILE, IT WORKED. IT REALLY WORKED. THERE WERE ONLY THIRTEEN OF US -- TO KEEP SOME CONSENSUS. A RUSSIAN, A FEW OF US EUROPEANS, DEAR YONIYOKO, OF COURSE, A NEW ZEALANDER, A COUPLE OF AMERICANS... WE WERE A HIGH-POWERED BUNCH. TWO NOBEL PRIZE WINNERS, MYSELF INCLUDED.
ALMOST FROM THE BEGINNING OUR CONCERNS WERE TERRITORIAL. HELPING TO DIVIDE THE WORLD UP. REGULATING LITTLE WARS SO THEY DIDN'T BECOME BIG WARS, KEEPING DICTATORSHIPS FROM GETTING TOO FULL OF THEMSELVES. WE BECAME THE WORLD'S DOMESTICS, CLEANING UP WHEREVER THE DIRT GOT TOO THICK. IT WAS A GREAT RESPONSIBILITY, BUT WE SHOULDERED IT QUITE HAPPILY. IT RATHER PLEASED US, AT THE BEGINNING, TO THINK THAT WE THIRTEEN WERE SHAPING THE WORLD, AND THAT NOBODY BUT THE HIGHEST ECHELONS OF GOVERNMENT KNEW THAT WE EVEN EXISTED.

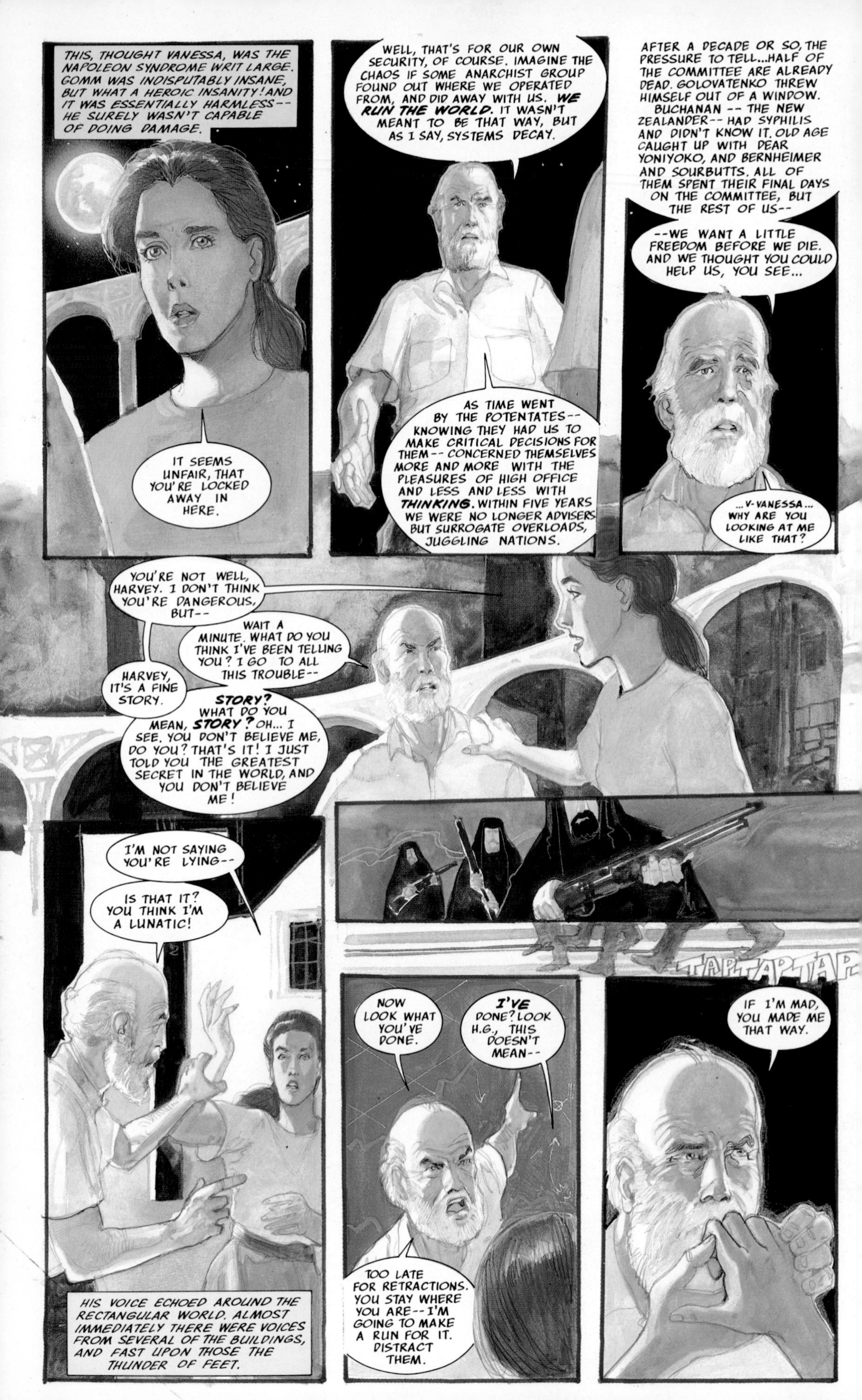
THIS, THOUGHT VANESSA, WAS THE NAPOLEON SYNDROME WRIT LARGE. GOMM WAS INDISPUTABLY INSANE, BUT WHAT A HEROIC INSANITY! AND IT WAS ESSENTIALLY HARMLESS-- HE SURELY WASN'T CAPABLE OF DOING DAMAGE.
IT SEEMS UNFAIR, THAT YOU'RE LOCKED AWAY IN HERE.
WELL, THAT'S FOR OUR OWN SECURITY, OF COURSE. IMAGINE THE CHAOS IF SOME ANARCHIST GROUP FOUND OUT WHERE WE OPERATED FROM, AND DID AWAY WITH US. WE RUN THE WORLD. IT WASN'T MEANT TO BE THAT WAY, BUT AS I SAY, SYSTEMS DECAY.
AS TIME WENT BY THE POTENTATES-- KNOWING THEY HAD US TO MAKE CRITICAL DECISIONS FOR THEM-- CONCERNED THEMSELVES MORE AND MORE WITH THE PLEASURES OF HIGH OFFICE AND LESS AND LESS WITH THINKING. WITHIN FIVE YEARS WE WERE NO LONGER ADVISERS BUT SURROGATE OVERLOADS, JUGGLING NATIONS.
AFTER A DECADE OR SO, THE PRESSURE TO TELL...HALF OF THE COMMITTEE ARE ALREADY DEAD. GOLOVATENKO THREW HIMSELF OUT OF A WINDOW. BUCHANAN -- THE NEW ZEALANDER-- HAD SYPHILIS AND DIDN'T KNOW IT. OLD AGE CAUGHT UP WITH DEAR YONIYOKO, AND BERNHEIMER AND SOURBUTTS. ALL OF THEM SPENT THEIR FINAL DAYS ON THE COMMITTEE, BUT THE REST OF US--
--WE WANT A LITTLE FREEDOM BEFORE WE DIE. AND WE THOUGHT YOU COULD HELP US, YOU SEE...
...V-VANESSA... WHY ARE YOU LOOKING AT ME LIKE THAT?
YOU'RE NOT WELL, HARVEY. I DON'T THINK YOU'RE DANGEROUS, BUT--
WAIT A MINUTE. WHAT DO YOU THINK I'VE BEEN TELLING YOU? I GO TO ALL THIS TROUBLE--
HARVEY, IT'S A FINE STORY.
STORY? WHAT DO YOU MEAN, STORY? OH... I SEE. YOU DON'T BELIEVE ME, DO YOU? THAT'S IT! I JUST TOLD YOU THE GREATEST SECRET IN THE WORLD, AND YOU DON'T BELIEVE ME!
I'M NOT SAYING YOU'RE LYING--
IS THAT IT? YOU THINK I'M A LUNATIC!
HIS VOICE ECHOED AROUND THE RECTANGULAR WORLD. ALMOST IMMEDIATELY THERE WERE VOICES FROM SEVERAL OF THE BUILDINGS, AND FAST UPON THOSE THE THUNDER OF FEET.
TAPTAPTAP
NOW LOOK WHAT YOU'VE DONE.
I'VE DONE? LOOK H.G., THIS DOESN'T MEAN--
TOO LATE FOR RETRACTIONS. YOU STAY WHERE YOU ARE-- I'M GOING TO MAKE A RUN FOR IT. DISTRACT THEM.
IF I'M MAD, YOU MADE ME THAT WAY.

PTOW PTOW

HOLD IT RIGHT THERE!
ALL RIGHT.

MEA CULPA!

WHAT ARE YOU DOING OUT AT THIS TIME OF NIGHT?
JUST STAR GAZING, THAT'S ALL.
YOU WEREN'T ALONE.

THAT'S TRUE. I WASN'T ALONE.
VANESSA'S HEART SANK. THERE WAS NO ROUTE BACK TO HER ROOM WITHOUT CROSSING THE OPEN COURTYARD; AND EVEN NOW, WITH THE ALARM RAISED, GUILLEMOT WOULD PROBABLY BE CHECKING ON HER.
HAD SHE OFFENDED THE OLD MAN SO MUCH HE WAS NOW GOING TO BETRAY HER?
I SAW THE WOMAN YOU BROUGHT IN--
WHERE?
CLIMBING OVER THE WALL.
JESUS WEPT!
I SAID TO HER. I SAID, YOU'LL BREAK YOUR NECK CLIMBING OVER THE WALL. YOU'D BE BETTER WAITING UNTIL THEY OPEN THE GATE--
OPEN THE GATE. HE WASN'T SUCH A LUNATIC, AFTER ALL.
PHILLIPENKO, ESCORT HARVEY BACK TO HIS DORMITORY. THE REST OF YOU, FOLLOW ME!

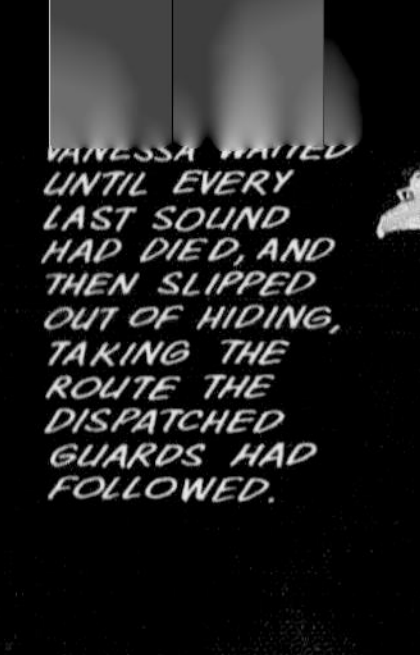
VANESSA WAITED UNTIL EVERY LAST SOUND HAD DIED, AND THEN SLIPPED OUT OF HIDING, TAKING THE ROUTE THE DISPATCHED GUARDS HAD FOLLOWED.

AS THE OLD MAN HAD PROTESTED WHEN THEY'D FIRST MET, SECURITY **WAS** WOEFULLY INADEQUATE, AND SHE THANKED GOD FOR IT.

SOME CHOCOLATE, MRS. JAPE?

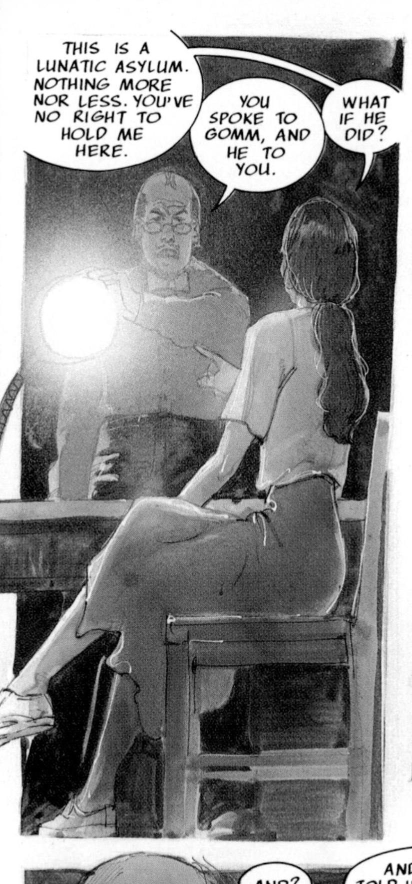

THIS IS A LUNATIC ASYLUM. NOTHING MORE NOR LESS. YOU'VE NO RIGHT TO HOLD ME HERE.
YOU SPOKE TO GOMM, AND HE TO YOU.
WHAT IF HE DID?

WHAT DID HE TELL YOU?
I WANT TO KNOW, MRS. JAPE.
WHAT NONSENSE DID HE TELL YOU? I'D LIKE TO KNOW, MRS. JAPE. HUMOR ME.

HE TOLD ME NONSENSE. HE'S INSANE. I THINK YOU'RE ALL INSANE.
HE SAID THERE WAS SOME KIND OF COMMITTEE AT WORK HERE THAT MADE DECISIONS ABOUT WORLD POLITICS AND THAT HE WAS ONE OF THEM. THAT WAS IT, FOR WHAT IT'S WORTH.

AND?
AND I GENTLY TOLD HIM HE WAS OUT OF HIS MIND.
MR. GOMM IS A PARANOID SCHIZOPHRENIC. HE CAN BE EXTREMELY DANGEROUS, GIVEN HALF A CHANCE. YOU WERE PRETTY LUCKY.
AND THE OTHERS? HE'S NOT ALONE. I'VE HEARD THEM.
THEY'RE ALL DERANGED, THOUGH THEIR CONDITIONS VARY. AND IN THEIR TIME, UNLIKELY AS IT MAY SEEM, THEY'VE ALL BEEN KILLERS. SOME OF THEM MULTIPLE KILLERS. THAT'S WHY THEY HAVE THE PLACE TO THEMSELVES, HIDDEN AWAY.
THAT'S WHY THE OFFICERS ARE ARMED.

VANESSA WAS ABOUT TO ASK WHY THEY WERE REQUIRED TO MASQUERADE AS NUNS, BUT KLEIN WAS NOT ABOUT TO GIVE HER AN OPPORTUNITY.
BELIEVE ME, IT'S AS INCONVENIENT FOR ME AS IT IS IRRITATING FOR YOU TO BE HERE.
THEN LET ME GO.

WHEN MY INVESTIGATIONS ARE COMPLETE. IN THE MEANWHILE, YOUR COOPERATION WOULD BE APPRECIATED. IF MR. GOMM OR ANY OTHER PATIENT TRIES TO CO-OPT YOU INTO SOME PLAN OR OTHER, PLEASE REPORT THEM TO ME IMMEDIATELY. WILL YOU DO THAT?
I SUPPOSE--
AND PLEASE REFRAIN FROM ANY FURTHER ESCAPE ATTEMPTS. THE NEXT ONE COULD PROVE FATAL.

WHICH, OF ALL THE ROUTES TO THE TRUTH THAT LAY BEFORE HER, WAS THE UNLIKELIEST PATH? SHE HAD BEEN GIVEN SEVERAL ALTERNATIVES: BY GOMM, BY KLEIN, BY HER OWN COMMON SENSE. ALL OF THEM WERE TEMPTINGLY IMPROBABLE. ALL, LIKE THE PATH THAT HAD BROUGHT HER HERE, UNMARKED AS TO THEIR FINAL DESTINATION.
SHE SUFFERED THE CONSEQUENCE OF HER PERVERSITY IN FOLLOWING THAT TRACK OF COURSE; HERE SHE WAS, WEARY AND BATTERED, LOCKED UP WITH LITTLE HOPE OF ESCAPE. BUT THAT PERVERSITY WAS HER NATURE -- PERHAPS, AS RONALD HAD ONCE SAID, THE ONE INDISPUTABLE FACT ABOUT HER. IF SHE DISREGARDED THAT INSTINCT NOW, DESPITE ALL IT HAD BROUGHT HER TO, SHE WAS LOST. SHE LAY AWAKE, TURNING THE AVAILABLE ALTERNATIVES OVER IN HER HEAD. BY MORNING SHE HAD MADE UP HER MIND.
SHE WAITED ALL DAY, HOPING GOMM WOULD COME, BUT SHE WASN'T SURPRISED WHEN HE FAILED TO SHOW. IT WAS POSSIBLE THAT EVENTS OF THE PREVIOUS EVENING HAD LANDED HIM IN DEEPER TROUBLE THAN EVEN HE COULD TALK HIS WAY OUT OF.
GUILLEMOT CAME AND WENT, WITH FOOD, WITH DRINK -- AND IN THE MIDDLE OF THE AFTERNOON -- WITH PLAYING CARDS.
SHE PICKED UP THE GIST OF FIVE-CARD POKER QUITE RAPIDLY, AND THEY PASSED A CONTENTED HOUR OR TWO PLAYING, WHILE THE AIR CARRIED SHOUTS FROM THE COURTYARD WHERE THE BEDLAMITES WERE RACING FROGS.
DO YOU THINK YOU COULD ARRANGE FOR ME TO HAVE A BATH, OR AT LEAST A SHOWER?
IT'S GETTING SO THAT I DON'T LIKE MY OWN COMPANY.
I'LL FIND OUT FOR YOU.
WOULD YOU? THAT'S VERY KIND.
HE RETURNED AN HOUR LATER TO TELL HER THAT DISPENSATION HAD BEEN SOUGHT AND GRANTED.
WOULD YOU LIKE TO ACCOMPANY ME TO THE SHOWERS?
ARE YOU GOING TO SCRUB MY BACK?
PLEASE FOLLOW ME.
THE FACILITIES HE BROUGHT HER TO WERE FAR FROM PRIMITIVE, AND SHE REGRETTED, WALKING INTO THE MIRRORED BATHROOM, THAT ACTUALLY WASHING WAS NOT HIGH ON HER LIST OF PRIORITIES.
I'LL BE OUTSIDE THE DOOR.
THAT'S REASSURING.

IVORY
OH, GUILLEMOT!
TUMP
D-DON'T SHOOT.

NOW... YOU'RE GOING TO TAKE ME TO MR. GOMM AND THE OTHERS. QUICKLY AND QUIETLY.
AND IF YOU TRY TO DO ANYTHING CLEVER, I'LL SHOOT YOU IN THE BACK. I KNOW IT'S NOT VERY MANLY, BUT THEN I'M NOT A MAN. I'M JUST AN UNPREDICTABLE WOMAN. SO TREAT ME VERY CAREFULLY.
HE LED HER OUT OF THE BUILDING AND THROUGH A SERIES OF PASSAGEWAYS THAT TOOK THEM-- OR SO SHE GUESSED-- TOWARD THE BELL TOWER AND THE COMPLEX THAT CLUSTERED ABOUT IT.
SHE HAD ALWAYS ASSUMED THIS, THE HEART OF THE FORTRESS, TO BE A CHAPEL. SHE COULD NOT HAVE BEEN MORE WRONG.
IT BRIEFLY OCCURRED TO HER THAT THE PLACE HAD BEEN BUILT TO WITHSTAND A NUCLEAR ATTACK, AN IMPRESSION REINFORCED BY THE FACT THAT THE CORRIDORS ALL LED DOWN. IF THIS WAS AN ASYLUM, IT WAS BUILT TO HOUSE SOME RARE LUNATICS.
WELL-- NOT MUCH HAPPENING TODAY.
WHAT IS THIS PLACE?
WE CALL IT THE BOUDOIR. IT'S WHERE EVERYTHING HAPPENS.
GOD DAMN IT!

SHIT.
I'M GOING TO SHOOT YOU DEAD.
WHERE'S GOMM AND THE OTHERS?
DOWN THE HALL. TURN LEFT AND LEFT AGAIN.
BREEE BREEE
WHAT'S GOING ON?
WHY ALL THE COMMOTION?
BREEE
P. GOMM
VANESSA! YOU CAME, EH? YOU CAME!
BREEE

BREEE BREEE
WAKE UP, YOU OLD BUGGERS.
THE ALARM'S RINGING.
THEY'LL BE HERE SOON
BUT WE'RE OUTNUMBERED. WE'LL NEVER GET OUT ALIVE.
SHE'S RIGHT. IT'S NO USE.
SAVE THE WHALES
BR
BREE
SHUT UP, GOLDBERG. SHE'S GOT A GUN, HASN'T SHE?
ONE. ONE GUN AGAINST ALL OF THEM.
I'M GOING BACK TO BED.
THIS IS A CHANCE TO ESCAPE. PROBABLY THE ONLY CHANCE WE'LL EVER GET.
AND WHAT ABOUT THE GAMES?
FORGET THE GAMES. LET THEM STEW AWHILE.
IT'S TOO LATE. HEAR THAT-- THEY'RE COMING. WE'RE TRAPPED.
GOOD.
YOU ARE INSANE.
YOU CAN STILL SHOOT US.
I DON'T WANT TO GET OUT OF HERE THAT MUCH.
THREATEN IT! THREATEN IT! TELL THEM IF THEY TRY ANYTHING YOU'LL SHOOT US ALL!
BRE...
BE GENTLE.
SLAM!

PUT DOWN THE WEAPON, MRS. JAPE. TAKE IT FROM ME, YOU ARE COMPLETELY SURROUNDED.
I'LL KILL THEM ALL. I'M WARNING YOU. I'M DESPERATE. I'LL KILL THEM ALL BEFORE YOU SHOOT ME.
I SEE. AND WHY SHOULD YOU ASSUME THAT I GIVE A DAMN WHETHER YOU KILL THEM OR NOT? THEY'RE INSANE. I TOLD YOU THAT-- ALL LUNATICS, KILLERS...
WE BOTH KNOW THAT ISN'T TRUE.
I WANT THE FRONT GATES OPENED AND THE KEY IN THE IGNITION OF MY CAR. IF YOU TRY ANYTHING STUPID, MR. KLEIN, I WILL SYSTEMATICALLY SHOOT THESE HOSTAGES. NOW DISMISS YOUR BULLY-BOYS AND DO AS I SAY.
ALL RIGHT-- EVERYBODY OUT!
EVERY STEP THEY TOOK VANESSA EXPECTED A BULLET TO FIND HER, BUT MR. KLEIN WAS CLEARLY TOO CONCERNED FOR THE HEALTH OF THE ANCIENTS TO RISK CALLING HER BLUFF. THEY REACHED THE OPEN AIR WITHOUT INCIDENT.
POW!
BLAM!
GOMM, OPEN THE CAR DOORS.
AAGH!

BASTARDS!
CAN YOU DRIVE?
OF COURSE I CAN BLOODY DRIVE!
VRMM
THERE'S A TRACK, OFF THAT WAY.
WHICH WAY'S THAT WAY!?
RIGHT! RIGHT!
WHICH IS RIGHT?
FOR CHRIST'S SAKE--
I SEE IT! I SEE THE TRACK!

SCREEEEE
CRUNCH!

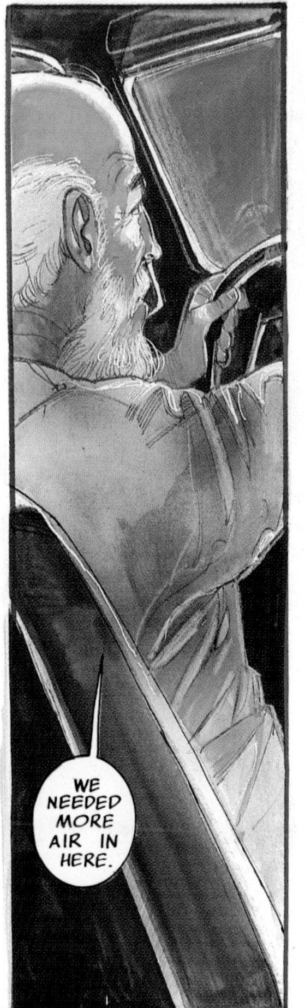
WE NEEDED MORE AIR IN HERE.

THEIRS WAS NOT THE ONLY ENGINE DISTURBING THE AEGEAN NIGHT. THERE WERE LIGHTS BEHIND THEM, AND THE SOUND OF HECTIC PURSUIT. WITH GUILLEMOT'S RIFLE LEFT IN THE CONVENT, THEY HAD NO SUDDEN DEATH TO BARGAIN WITH, AND KLEIN KNEW IT.
STEP ON IT! THEY'RE AFTER US.
I'M GOING AS FAST AS I CAN.
TURN OFF THE LIGHTS. IT'LL MAKE US LESS OF A TARGET.
THEN I WON'T BE ABLE TO SEE THE TRACK.
SO WHAT? YOU'RE NOT DRIVING ON IT ANYHOW.

MAYBE THE LOSS OF BLOOD WAS MAKING HER IRRESPONSIBLE, BUT VANESSA COULDN'T HELP LAUGHING. FOUR METHUSELAHS AND HERSELF IN A THREE-DOOR DRIVING AROUND IN THE DARK--ONLY A MADMAN WOULD HAVE TAKEN THIS SERIOUSLY.
AND THERE WAS THE FINAL AND INCONTESTABLE PROOF THAT THESE PEOPLE WEREN'T THE LUNATICS KLEIN HAD MARKED THEM AS, FOR THEY SAW THE HUMOR IN IT TOO.
SOMEWHERE OVER THE RAINBOW...
AND IF--AS HER DIZZIED MIND HAD CONCLUDED--THESE WERE CREATURES AS SANE AS HERSELF, THEN WHAT OF THE TALE THAT GOMM HAD TOLD? WAS THAT TRUE, TOO? WAS IT POSSIBLE THAT ARMAGEDDON HAD BEEN KEPT AT BAY BY THESE FEW GIGGLING GERIATRICS?
THERE! THERE'S ANOTHER TRACK! TRY THAT! TRY THAT!
THEY'RE GAINING ON US!
WHY, OH OH WHY CAN'T I...
SCREEEEEE
WE'RE NOT GOING TO MAKE IT. WE'RE ALL GOING TO DIE.
BLEEE!
ΣX 95
AΘHNA
WHERE ARE WE GOING?
HAVEN'T A CLUE, HAVE YOU?
WHEREVER THEY WERE HEADING, THEY WERE GOING AT A FAIR SPEED. THIS TRACK WAS FLATTER THAN THE ONE THEY'D LEFT, AND GOMM WAS TAKING FULL ADVANTAGE OF THE FACT.

WE'RE LOSING THEM! WE'RE LOSING THEM!
A COMMON EXHILARATION SEIZED ALL THE TRAVELERS NOW, AND THEY BEGAN TO SING ALONG WITH H.G. THEY WERE SINGING SO LOUDLY THAT GOMM COULDN'T HEAR MOTTERSHEAD INFORM HIM THAT THE ROAD AHEAD SEEMED TO DISAPPEAR.
...AND AWAKE UP WHERE THE CLOUDS ARE FAR...
VRRRRMM!
FLOYD?

A LITTLE WAY AHEAD IT SOUNDED AS IF A MAJOR ARGUMENT WAS GOING ON--DOZENS OF RAISED VOICES, IMPRECATIONS AND PLEADINGS.

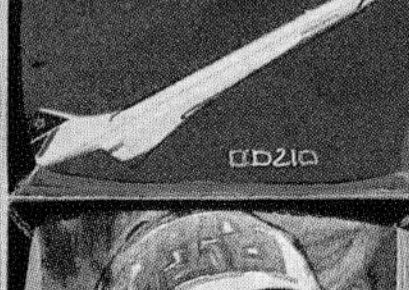

SHE LOOKED FROM SCREEN TO SCREEN: FROM WASHINGTON TO HAMBURG TO SYDNEY TO RIO DE JANEIRO. EVERYWHERE AROUND THE GLOBE THE MIGHTY WERE WAITING FOR NEWS. BUT THE ORACLES WERE DEAD.

THEY'RE JUST PERFORMERS.

THEY COULDN'T RUN A THREE-LEGGED RACE, NEVER MIND THE WORLD. THEY'RE GETTING HYSTERICAL, AND THEIR BUTTON FINGERS ARE STARTING TO ITCH.

WHAT AM I SUPPOSED TO DO ABOUT IT? I'M NO STRATEGIST.

NEITHER WERE GOMM AND THE OTHERS. THEY MIGHT HAVE BEEN, ONCE UPON A TIME, BUT THINGS SOON FELL APART.

SYSTEMS DECAY.

ISN'T **THAT** THE TRUTH. BY THE TIME I CAME HERE, HALF THE COMMITTEE WERE ALREADY DEAD. AND THE REST HAD LOST ALL INTEREST IN THEIR DUTIES--

BUT THEY STILL PROVIDED JUDGMENTS, AS H.G. SAID? THEY RULED THE WORLD?

AFTER A FASHION.

WHAT DO YOU MEAN... ***AFTER A FASHION?***

DIDN'T HE EXPLAIN? THEY PLAYED GAMES, MRS. JAPE. WHEN THEY BECAME BORED WITH SWEET REASON AND THE SOUND OF THEIR OWN VOICES, THEY GAVE UP DEBATE AND TOOK TO FLIPPING COINS.
NO.
AND RACING FROGS OF COURSE. THAT WAS ALWAYS A FAVORITE.
BUT THE GOVERNMENTS--SURELY THEY DIDN'T JUST ACCEPT...
YOU THINK THEY CARE? AS LONG AS THEY'RE IN THE PUBLIC EYE WHAT DOES IT MATTER TO THEM WHAT VERBIAGE THEY'RE SPOUTING, OR HOW IT WAS ARRIVED AT?
ALL CHANCE?
WHY NOT? IT HAS A VERY RESPECTABLE TRADITION. NATIONS HAVE FALLEN ON DECISIONS DIVINED FROM THE ENTRAILS OF SHEEP.
IT'S PREPOSTEROUS.
I AGREE. BUT I ASK YOU, IN ALL HONESTY, IS IT ANY MORE TERRIFYING THAN LEAVING THE POWER IN THEIR HANDS?
BETTER THE FROGS.

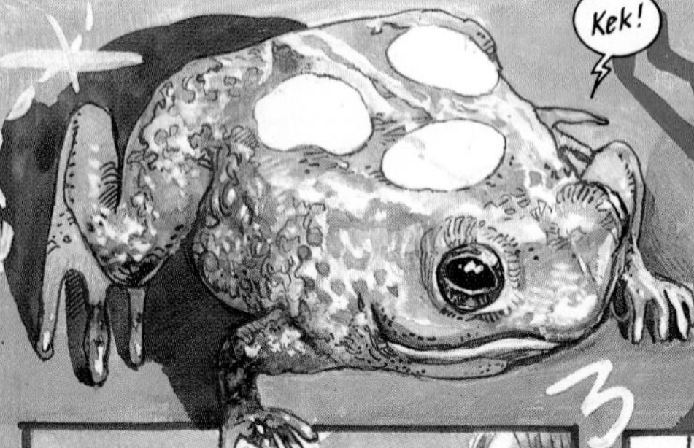

GOLDBERG'S FROG NOISE BROUGHT A CROAKING FROM EVERY CORNER OF THE COURTYARD. HEARING THE SOUND, VANESSA STIFLED A SMILE.

FARCE, SHE HAD TOLD HERSELF ONCE BEFORE, HAD TO BE PLAYED WITH A STRAIGHT FACE, AS THOUGH YOU BELIEVED EVERY OUTRAGEOUS WORD. ONLY TRAGEDY DEMANDED LAUGHTER--AND THAT, WITH THE AID OF THE FROGS, THEY MIGHT YET PREVENT.

END

ALSO PUBLISHED BY ECLIPSE GRAPHIC NOVELS

CLIVE BARKER'S

THE YATTERING AND JACK

Adapted by Steve Niles
Illustrated by John Bolton

A DARKLY HILARIOUS and weirdly perceptive tale of the devil at work from the acclaimed fantasist and master of horror fiction, Clive Barker.

Beelzebub sends his underling the Yattering to claim the soul of Jack Polo, pickle salesman. But in the Polo residence where the Yattering is bound, nothing doing. Polo's response, even to disaster, is merely to sigh, '*Que sera sera*'. The Yattering is going crazy. He must goad Polo to lunacy, the Old One insists. Polo was promised by his mother to the Lord of the Flies. And what match is a chronically dull pickle salesman for hell's own spawn . . . ? Find out.

Included in the same volume, a graphic adaptation of Clive Barker's short story *How Spoilers Bleed*, adapted by Steve Niles and Fred Burke, and illustrated by Hector Gomez. It tells of the gory revenge visited on white destroyers of the Brazilian jungle by the dying indigenous people of the Amazon basin. It is a punishment that fits the crime, incredibly unpleasant . . .

Clive Barker's bestselling works of fiction include *The Books of Blood*, *The Damnation Game*, *Weaveworld*, *Cabal*, *The Great and Secret Show*, *The Hellbound Heart*, *Imajica* and *The Thief of Always*. Not only is he prodigiously talented as a writer, he also produces and directs memorable films such as the *Hellraiser* trilogy, *Nightbreed* and *Candyman*, and is himself a spectacular visual artist. The illustrators he chooses to work with, therefore, John Bolton and Hector Gomez, are equally brilliant.

NEIL GAIMAN

MIRACLEMAN: THE GOLDEN AGE

Illustrated by Mark Buckingham

NEIL GAIMAN'S spectacular, mysterious, luminously strange and compelling saga of the all-British superhero and deity, Miracleman. *The Golden Age* is the age of miracles unimagined. It is the age of gods among men. It is the age of truth in which everything is what it seems, and nothing is as it was imagined.

'A work that transforms the superhero genre into something strange, wonderful, and politic. Excellent stuff!'

ALAN MOORE

MIRACLEMAN was given new life by Alan Moore, known as the King of the graphic novel, in the early 1980s. His and Gaiman's work is assessed in the critique below by Samuel R. Delany, author of *Dhalgren,* the *Nevèrÿon* series, and other science fiction masterpieces.

'Moore and Gaiman are the two writers who have done more to change the idea of what comics are and can be than anyone since . . . well, certainly since I started reading them in the 1940s. Reading Moore, followed by Gaiman, I found myself for the first time deeply, consistently, intensely interested in these comic book writers *as writers.* With that interest came a revision in the idea of what comics could be; they could be *written*, not just in a craftsman-like manner adequate to the visuals. The writing could be brilliant in itself. Here were writers with the range of language from silence to song - the whole of language with which to put across their stories. And the stories themselves! Gaiman's six entwined tales in *The Golden Age* come like sapphires afloat on a super-cooled liquid. They unfold like haiku. The voices they speak with are real. Their lambent characters, yearning both for bits of yesterday and portents of tomorrow, will linger with you long.'

SAMUEL R. DELANY